THE DOCTOR IN ARABIA
Eleanor Taylor Calverly and Grace Taylor Calverly

A CRUSADE
OF COMPASSION

FOR THE

HEALING OF THE NATIONS

A STUDY OF MEDICAL MISSIONS
FOR WOMEN AND CHILDREN

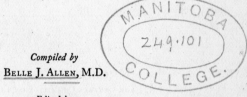

Compiled by
BELLE J. ALLEN, M.D.

Edited by
CAROLINE ATWATER MASON

"God had an only Son and He was a Missionary and a Physician"
DR. LIVINGSTONE

PUBLISHED BY
THE CENTRAL COMMITTEE ON THE UNITED STUDY OF FOREIGN MISSIONS
WEST MEDFORD, MASS.

The Vermont Printing Co.,
Brattleboro, Vermont, U. S. A.

FOREWORD

Upon the recommendation of the Committee of Twenty-eight "The Conservation of Human Life" was chosen for 1919-20 as the general theme for the text-books of the groups composing that committee. The Woman's Foreign Missionary section had long considered a study of Medical Missions and is glad to present this, its nineteenth text-book.

Dr. Allen has served as a medical missionary in India and has not only assembled much material from many lands, but has drawn on her own rich experience in the Butler Memorial Hospital at Baroda.

Mrs. Mason, who has given us two excellent study books, *Lux Christi* and *World Missions and World Peace*, has rendered valuable assistance to Dr. Allen and the Committee by adding to the material and putting it into form.

The usual reading list is omitted and reference is made in footnotes to the few available books of reference. It is hoped that Boards will publish in pamphlet form complete records of their medical missionaries and their work.

With the passing of the acute need for Red Cross and medical work in connection with the war, a need which women have met heroically, we earnestly appeal for their sympathetic study of the even greater age-long need of women and children, who live and die without any medical care whatever. Every argument and appeal for Red Cross work, for hospitals, ambulances, equipment, nurses and doctors, may be strengthened a hundredfold for medical missions for women and children in view of the numbers who suffer unattended on the great battlefield of motherhood and childhood.

To circulate this book widely among men and women is to render a great service to humanity and its Saviour. We no longer ask "who is my neighbor?" —That question has become an accusation. These world neighbors of ours need immediate aid. The Red Cross has taught us how to minister to the needs of our soldiers. The Cross of Christ alone can enable us to meet this greater need adequately.

MRS. HENRY W. PEABODY, *Chairman*.
MISS OLIVIA H. LAWRENCE.
MRS. FRANK MASON NORTH.
MRS. JAMES A. WEBB, JR.
MRS. A. V. POHLMAN.
MISS ALICE M. KYLE.
MISS GRACE T. COLBURN.

CONTENTS

LIST OF ILLUSTRATIONS

INTRODUCTION

THE general theme adopted for this year's study by the Committee of Twenty-eight is "The Conservation of Human Life." The very word "conservation" is filled today with new values, and carries with it a commendable practical note, which appeals. The need for it is intensified in these tragical days, beyond any other days in human experience. How to make sheltered women at home realize the need for conservation in non-Christian lands is a problem, for the conditions under which the majority of other women exist are almost unbelievable—unless they are experienced, seen and felt.

Effectually to change the conditions and carry the message of freedom to our neighbors across the seas will require a united effort, a tremendous effort, on the part of those who profess to know and follow our Lord and Saviour, Jesus Christ. All the eagerness, all the self-sacrificing devotion, all the purpose-to-win of the soldier will be necessary.

The harem woman, the zenana woman, the foot-bound, mind-bound woman has no Publicity Committee! Few may voice her needs, her suffering, her aspirations, her capacity to help to apply the remedy, which is for the healing of the nations.

What has been done is but a drop in the ocean of what may be done, nay, more, what must be done if women at home prove themselves worthy of the men and women who are laying down their lives for our freedom. The whole Church must be mobilized. No woman who seeks a worth-while task can afford to miss having a share in it. Closed hospitals, which a little self-denial might open; suffering children, unattended; women crying out inarticulately for help which you can give—this little handbook goes forth to try to make you hear that cry—and hearing it to respond. The response is the measure of your interest not in *them* or *it*, but in the Man, Christ Jesus, who is still saying today, "I have given you an example."

B. J. A.

DAUGHTER OF SCIENCE ~ PIONEER ~ THY TENDERNESS HATH BANISHED FEAR ~
WOMAN AND LEADER IN THEE BLEND, PHYSICIAN, SURGEON, STUDENT, FRIEND

BAS RELIEF WOMAN'S MEDICAL COLLEGE PHILADELPHIA

OUTLINE OF CHAPTER I.

THE BATTALION OF LIFE

A CRUSADE OF COMPASSION

CHAPTER I.

THE BATTALION OF LIFE

"Every non-Christian land is a land of pain."
A. J. Brown, D.D.

As the second decade of the twentieth century closes we hear much of the international mind. And well we may. Nationalism, over-stressed, hard, exclusive, self-centred, has been terribly displayed in the eyes of the whole world as carried to its logical limits: the purpose of supremacy for one nation over all others. Hence have come the great betrayal of civilization and all our woe.

Mighty reaction from such ultra-nationalism has seized upon us. The higher patriotism has been born, world-patriotism. At last the world is ready to declare all men to be brothers. Before the sorrows of devastated and broken peoples the nations strike hands in a league of compassion. Our strongest political, scientific, and financial intellects are set to work, together with hearts the tenderest, to organize availing help, to bind up the broken-hearted, to restore the maimed, the halt, and the blind, to build again the waste places of earth. This great arousal must not be permitted to fade as a passing phase of emotion,—a transient thing. Surely, this torrential stream of sympathy can be directed through channels broad, deep, and permanent toward the wide-world anguish hitherto so faintly recognized.

What of the Church of Christ in this hour of opportunity? This is the unparalleled crisis which demands sanctified statesmanship.

"There is a tide in the affairs of men,
  Which, taken at the flood, leads on to fortune,"
to spiritual as to temporal victory.

The Church's new day.   The Church shows herself ready to open her places of worship for kindly deeds and measures of relief; she gives discreetly of her material wealth; she responds sincerely to appeals perpetually made upon her compassion, but is there danger that after all she may miss the hour's supreme challenge? that she may fail to know that this is indeed her day? For, "in a minute it is going to strike twelve on the clock of the world; what we do now we do forever." The tide of the passion for humanity, now at the flood, proceeds from the heart of the compassionate Christ who so loved the world that He offered Himself a willing sacrifice for its sin and sorrow; it is a Christ-like thing, the Church's own. To her great day may the Church in America awake, rejoicing as a strong man to run a race, entering with new hope and moral earnestness upon the glorious world-saving enterprise, begun in time of war a century ago. Let her plans of campaign be bigger, bolder, braver than ever. Let her fill her premier place as she was first among us to initiate the international mind even in the day of things small and provincial, when the United States had hardly attained national consciousness; let her claim her right to count as pioneer in the new internationalism, for her horizon for a hundred years has been bounded, not by America, not by Europe, but by Asia, Africa, the Islands of the Seas. It is the Church's right to lead in the new day, not to follow; to go forth as the morning, fair as the moon, clear as the sun, terrible as an army with banners.

A soldier's testimony.   A British soldier, one of "Kitchener's men," lying wounded to the death, early in the war, wrote to friends at home as follows:

"Lying here in the hospital, helpless three months from shrapnel wounds which refuse to heal, I have been thinking. You know I have been all over the world. It would seem that I should have plenty to think about. Strange, isn't it, that my thoughts always go back to the one theme of foreign missions, especially as I never thought of them before but in derision; yes, and that notwithstanding help cheerfully given me at mission hospitals. I do not remember giving a single penny to foreign missions in my life. It was so easy to prate about their uselessness, all so cheap and popular, too. Even as I traveled in distant lands, sometimes well-knowing that but for the work of missionaries there had been no road for me, I still refused to own the blessings that were conferred on the natives. I think that stranger even than my ingratitude for help generously given me in mission hospitals, for gold was my God. My whole energies were set on trade. I might in common fairness have recognized who prepared the way for markets which I found so profitable, but I did not. When the call to arms came, as you will remember I told you in an earlier letter, I was in London, home on furlough. I joined Lord Kitchener's men. You sent me a New Testament. I have it now. Reading at random one night for want of something better to do, I was struck by the words of John 17:3: "And this is life eternal, that they might know Thee, the only true God, and Jesus Christ whom Thou hast sent." I could not forget those words. They have been with me every waking hour these twelve months. They are with me now, and who can tell how precious I find them? They caused me to care not a jot for this poor, maimed body, soon to be set aside. I have found a Friend, oh! such a Friend, and I realize now that this Friend cares for every savage of our race, even as He cares for me, and why should He not? Ah, there is the secret of my contempt for foreign missions. I had not then thought of life eternal. Would God I had earlier known the new birth. I envy you fellows who have done so much for the cause. I would gladly die for it now when it is too late. As I think of the loyalty of subject races so gloriously exhibited in this day of stress; as I picture those splendid Indians seen in France, my mind still refuses to absorb anything but the great central fact—we have here the fruition of the work of British missionaries and of the prayers of missionary-hearted men. It is sweet to die for England. I do not regret it. It is sweet to see the devotion of tender nurses about our beds. A few vagrant thoughts flutter for a moment over these consolations. But to die in glory of contemplation of what it is to minister and to die in service for the King of kings! That will never be my part. Perhaps it might have been had somebody taken me in hand early enough. Why does the Church keep foreign missions so much in the background? How is it that I was left so long a scoffer? I do not blame any mortal. I am saying that something is wrong with a scheme of things which fails to put the whole world for Christ right in the forefront as *the battle-cry of the Christian Church*."

I. *The Battalion*

The conception of the host of Christ's followers as an advancing army, of the spread of Christ's Kingdom as a holy warfare with the forces of sin, has been familiar through the ages from St. Paul to Bishop Heber. Vast regions, indeed, remain unconquered still, but like a mighty army the Church of God still moves on, bringing good tidings, publishing peace and salvation. As the Son of God goes forth to war we observe among those who follow in His train one battalion strangely silent, although in full order of battle.

This battalion marches forward without glittering insignia, waving banners or thrill of martial music, but it keeps step with the main army, knows the same discipline of obedience and self-denial, advances under the same leadership toward the one objective. That objective is the conservation of human life in two worlds, that which now is and that which is to come; and with this we find enfolded, as the flower is enfolded in the bud, the lifting-up of men and women and young children from present misery and degradation to a decent human plane of living where are found purity and peace, hope and joy.

When we perceive the full purpose of the advancing host of the Prince of Peace we recognize this silent division with a thrill of emotion;—it is the Battalion of Life!

For this company embodies love in action, being composed of men and women of the Order of the Great Physician, who go forth in His Name to the service of the sick and sorrowful and oppressed in the dark places of the earth. We name them medical missionaries.

Sacredness of human life. On the eve of his departure for France one of the new recruits, a colored lad, said to another simply, "I am ready to fight, glad to die if need be to defend just plain human rights. They are worth dying for." Plain human rights! And the first of these is the right to live. The sacredness of human life is a conception peculiar to Christianity; to vindicate that conception and to establish it is essentially the aim of the Battalion of Life. The challenge comes to the whole Church. These soldiers of Christ believe that, being created in God's image, every man and woman, whether born in the Occident or in the Orient, has a sacred right to life temporal and life eternal, and to conditions of life, if not little lower than those of angels, at least a little higher than those of beasts of the field. Where they go, in place of despair, torment, corruption, life and peace spring up as of old when Jesus walked in Galilee.

The Commission. From whom has the Battalion of Life received its call and commission?

He sent them to preach the Kingdom of God and to heal the sick.

And Jesus went about all the cities and villages, teaching in their synagogues and preaching the gospel of the Kingdom and healing every sickness and every disease among the people. But when He saw the multitudes, He was moved with compassion on them, because they fainted and were scattered abroad. . . And when He had called his twelve disciples, He gave them power over unclean spirits to cast them out, and to heal all manner of disease. . . . And Jesus said, Freely ye have received, freely give.

The Great Physician calls for volunteers for His Battalion of Life and thus commissions them. Call and commission are alike divine.

II. Need for the Battalion

It may be briefly said that the need for medical missions is as imperative as the wireless call S.O.S. which no ship sailing the seven seas ignores. It is imperious, imperative, importunate.

Vastness of need. The heathen nations (phrase which in general connotes the nations destitute of enlightened theory or practice of sanitation, disease prevention, medicine, or surgery) number about one billion. This estimate includes two hundred and two million Moslems, not technically included in the term heathen. Arrayed over against these ignorant and suffering masses the Christian world has now in the field a force of one thousand and eleven missionary physicians, of which number

about three hundred are women. In addition there
are two hundred and sixty-seven native Christian
practitioners. An illustration of the condition of
need here indicated is given by the statement of
the Imperial Gazetteer of India, in a late issue,
that "even in large towns the great majority die
without having been seen by any person competent
to diagnose the case." The six thousand human
beings who die without medical relief every year
in a city like Calcutta are a mere fraction of the
rate of preventable mortality throughout the remote
villages and rural districts. This in some regions
reaches sixty-two per cent. of the whole number
of deaths.

Inadequately have these facts been realized in
the hearts and minds of Christian people. When
this realization dawns who can doubt that millions
of dollars will be poured forth for the succor of
humanity in darkened lands with the same generous spirit shown by our country in the relief of
suffering in Europe? Not less surely will the ranks
of the Battalion be filled with loyal soldiers and
servants of the Great Physician.

Superstition and ignorance prime causes of need. Not alone in the immensity of need
do we hear the ring of this challenge,
but in the pathos of the suffering
resulting from spiritual oppression. Are our ears
sensitive to the S.O.S. call of humanity? Have we
ever *seriously* asked ourselves what business we
have to be indifferent to human need? Is there
not warning enough given in the dehumanizing
effect of such an attitude of indifference? "O that
we had eyes to see and ears to hear!"

The wounded in battle, the sick and suffering in Europe today appeal to us, because the mind is kept constantly reminded through publicity measures. They may be our own or near to us in some way and our realization is greater. Millions are poured forth for meeting their need and ought to be. Shall we remain blind and deaf to this other greater call? What would be the result if with our expeditionary force there were no medical corps; if the barest rudiments of sanitation and hygiene were undreamed of? What if the Red Cross and all it stands for in self-sacrificing ministrations had never entered the heart of man to conceive, much less to execute? What if there were no generous and compassionate public constantly back of it all, making possible these gentle ministrations? What if there were no knowledge of surgery to restore our wounded boys?—if insanity were thought to be a form of demoniacal possession, and the insane were chained to rocks and left to die or buried alive?

Native practices. Suppose all of our own sick were objects of loathing or of fear? Suppose they knew only how to suffer, but were strangers to relief from suffering? Suppose the best treatment known for pneumonia were to burn a hole through the chest with a red-hot iron, and this ignorance was the work of religious leaders or of the priests? Suppose your only child were burned and the native physician only knew how to prescribe the cow-dung poultice? Or suppose your child were needlessly blind, because of the ignorance or neglect or both of attendants at its birth? Suppose you were enduring the lancinating pain of ophthalmia, and sight depended upon intelligent care? Suppose 'the specialist' should prescribe a solution of red peppers or pierce the eye with a needle and take the sight out with it? Suppose you were the mother of a family, ill nigh unto death, and 'the family physician,' after exhausting all of his decoctions of snake stews and spiders' legs, provided the panacea—milk in which the toe of the priest had been washed?

But suppose it were only the toothache and after tying up toes and arms and legs with sacred threads and bits of wood you were dominated by the fear of losing the eye if the tooth were drawn, because your priest told you so? But beyond the treatment of disease, suppose your priest keeps you ignorant of the causes of disease? Suppose you firmly believe that people about you—anyone—can 'wish upon you' such harm that all your life is spent in fear of the evil eye? You blacken your child's eyelids so the Evil Eye will not recognize it, and call it by a false name to mislead the evil spirit bent on afflicting it. Suppose 'the family doctor,' who is also a prophet and priest, only knows enough to warn you of the prevalence of evil spirits, and you pay him well to propitiate them and protect you from their presence? Suppose it is by his authority that you are ignorant and, notwithstanding his promised protection, disease stalks unbidden and unrecognized into your house in the form of plague or fever or cholera, and he only knows enough to exact tribute and yet more tribute to exorcise these evil spirits, assuring you the pestilence is all due, no doubt, to the curse of the women folks in the house? Suppose he assures you that the "Western way" will cause your house to be burned down, or only daughters to be born to your house or that your only son will be taken? And suppose you know no other way, because this ego-maniac has decreed that wisdom will die with him?

Suppose your whole life is one perpetual bondage to fear—fear of malevolence in some insidious form, lurking to spring upon you; fear of spirits, fear of hot remedies, fear of cold ones, fear of milk, fear of fruit, fear of water, fear of shadows, fear of sounds, fear of tears, so that the child who weeps must be fed opium to keep that evil spirit quiet and you know no other way? Would your ears be gladdened by the knowledge of a better cure than these? So would those of heathen women! Would you rejoice in your innermost being that a sovereign remedy had been found? So would they! Would you be thankful from the depths of your being that the Battalion of Life had heard your call and were coming *in numbers large enough* to meet the need? So would they! Would you not be glad to have a share in providing a fighting chance for innocent childhood? Would you not be overjoyed to have a hand at breaking the shackles of imprisoned womanhood?

The Great Physician calls for volunteers for the Battalion of Life. This is much, but it is not all. Not only is the challenge heard in the immensity of the extent of need and the measure of relievable human suffering due to ignorance, but the challenge comes also in the character of service—a service no less heroic than that on the battlefields of France. It must be as unspectacular as the courage displayed by those brave soldiers who deliberately dared wasting illness in order that millions of other lads might be spared the suffering of trench fever, but in quality and kind it is a service unsurpassed even by that.

Testimony of a famous traveler. Says Isabella Bird Bishop: "I have traveled for more than seven years in Asia and as a traveler entirely unconnected with missions except by sympathy and interest. As a traveler, I desire to bear the very strongest testimony that can be borne to the blessings of medical missions wherever they can be carried on as they ought to be. On the western frontier of China, I would say that a medical missionary might do more than twenty evangelistic missionaries at the present time, and there is room, I was going to say, for fifty medical missionaries in the world where there is but one now, and not only room for them but a claim for them."

Conservation of child life. That cleanliness is a next-door neighbor of godliness is a truism which needs no demonstration: that cleanliness is vital to healthy human life, and in an especial measure to child life, is a no less familiar fact in Western civilization. But not so in the East. Water for drinking purposes is drawn from rivers or tanks used as public bathing places. The most elementary rules of sanitary care are disregarded, because wholly unknown. No wonder that infant mortality reaches an appalling rate. Here we cannot stress *cure* of the numberless filth diseases; *prevention* is first and last the cardinal principle. Every Christian hospital and dispensary is a social centre, not for healing alone, but for the distribution of the axioms of cleanliness. And the method works where it can be applied.

A questionnaire. Some months ago the editor of this book sent out a number of copies of a printed circular containing twenty-nine questions to missionary physicians, both men and women, in India, Korea, the Philippines, and China. Question number 16 is as follows: "Is anything done in prenatal or postnatal care?" Out of twenty filled-in questionnaires taken at random from the mass, only four answers to this question are *yes*, and this answer is qualified by mention of the favorable results having come through missionary efforts. Desperation rings in one answer, "No. Hopeless, because of lack of cleanliness." But full of promise as of pathos is the occasional two-word reply: "*Not yet*."

Another question (number 13) reads: "Is anything done to conserve human life, outside of missionary or governmental activities?" To this the answers read variously, "Very, very little," "Practically nil," "No!" "God looks after most of the poor out here" (this last from Korea from one whose nearest foreign fellow-physician is two hundred miles away, nearest hospital two hundred miles, nearest dentist five hundred miles distant). Another reports her nearest medical neighbor and hospital distant an eight-days' journey. Under question 18, concerning epidemics, occurs the sub-question, "What is the root cause of them?" With startling monotony come the answers: "Filth," "Dirt," "Uncleanliness and ignorance," "Filth and superstition," "Overcrowding and dirt," "Ignorance, prejudice, pollution of water," etc. One answers laconically, "Lack of doctors." Involuntarily rises before one the picture of smug city blocks, here at home, with a shining plate at every other door bearing a physician's name and title, and within, perchance, a qualified man or woman, looking out anxiously for the patients who do not come.

The pity of it, and yet again, the pity of it!

III. Personnel of the Battalion

In describing the Battalion of Life we noted that it was made up of men and women, the latter, indeed, somewhat in the minority, but holding their own valorously.

The question arises, Do women belong in the profession of medicine and, in particular, are they fitted for the peculiarly difficult conditions to be encountered on heathen ground?

The first division of the question seems to have answered itself in the United States and Great Britain where medical women have now won for themselves assured standing. It was not always so. Women in medicine. The story reads like a tale of the dim past and yet we have to go back but two generations to reach its beginnings. "Mentally, morally, and physically unfit," was the dictum of authority in the profession.

All the soldier's courage, heroism, and invincible "dogged as does it" were demonstrated by the pio-

DR. GURUBAI KARMARKAR
Bombay, India

neers of the woman's medical work. Offensive language was heaped upon the early students; hisses, caterwaulings, yells, missiles greeted their appearance in the amphitheatre.

The medical fraternities in all lands took up the burden of opposition. Elizabeth Blackwell encountered it when she had to apply to twelve different institutions in 1849 before the faculty of the Geneva Medical College finally admitted her within its doors. "Conservative women" drew aside their skirts when she met them in church. No respectable roof in New York would shelter her for an office, and she was obliged to buy a house in which to practice.

"Dr. Elizabeth Shattuck,* who was graduated in 1854, entered upon her career with the thought of becoming a medical missionary—probably the first woman to entertain such a wild idea. After graduating she sought opportunity for hospital experience without success, but her determination to reach her heart's desire was such that at length she applied as head nurse at the Philadelphia Hospital. After three years of hard work she applied to her mission board only to be refused because she was *unmarried*. Later, when Vassar College was established, Dr. Shattuck was appointed resident physician and professor of physiology and hygiene.

"A group of Quakers, a sect which has never hesitated to champion a cause which it deemed just even though public sentiment might be against it, through the medium of Dr. Bartholomew Fussel,

---

*Address by Dr. Ellen R. Potter of Woman's Medical College.

a physician of repute in Chester County, seems to have evolved first the idea of a medical school for women, the foundation of his thought being that women should have the same opportunity in life as men. A group of those interested in the cause secured a charter in the name of the Female Medical College of Pennsylvania, March 11, 1850. Every obstacle conceivable was put in the way by the then-existing authorities. As late as 1859 resolutions of excommunication were issued against every physician who should teach in the school, every woman graduated from it and everybody else who should consult with such teachers. Nevertheless, the effort was not in vain. The Woman's Medical College of Pennsylvania has not only prospered, but has prepared more women as medical missionaries than any other institution in the United States."

The first woman physician in England was treated with scorn and rudeness and amazement when she entered upon the study of medicine. One physician, more tolerant than the rest, said, "Why not be a nurse?" and the kindly old doctor yielded finally to her importunities under a definite agreement that she was to dress like a nurse and promise seriously not to look too intelligent.

Status of women in the Orient. It is needless to enlarge upon the oppressive attitude of the men of the Orient toward women, but a few words are called for on this point since the woman medical missionary finds just here prime justification for her presence. In India the Code of Manu, older than the Law of Moses, settled the status of Hindu womanhood. "Though destitute of every virtue, or seeking pleasure elsewhere, or devoid of good qualities, yet a husband must be constantly worshipped as a god by a faithful wife." (Manu V, section 154.) "Sinful woman must be as foul as falsehood itself. This is a fixed law." (Manu IX.) Common proverbs run like the following: "He is a fool who considers his wife as his friend." "Educating a woman is like putting a knife in the hands of a monkey."

In China the inferior position of women is less formally declared, but in practice there is little to choose. "The social system is terribly deficient in providing for the natural and divine rights of women." (Dr. A. H. Smith.) To illustrate: A missionary woman physician was called on to treat a sick woman in Canton. The family was poor and the one comfortable chamber in the forlorn house was occupied by a big buffalo or "water-cow," while the sufferer lay in a stifling inner room. The missionary begged the husband to reverse this arrangement. The man objected. "If I put my wife in that room and my buffalo in the inner room, the buffalo may get sick as my wife has got sick," he demurred.

"But your wife will die if she stays there," protested the physician. "Give her a good room."

"But if I give the buffalo the poor room," persisted the husband, "and he gets sick, he will die; and it costs more to buy a buffalo than it does to buy a woman."

Buddhism, although driven out of India, is the religion of millions of the people of the East, including Burma, Ceylon, Siam, China, and Japan. One sentiment of Buddha suffices to show forth the position of woman among his followers: Buddha rejoiced that he had escaped three curses: that he was not born in hell, or as a vermin, or as a woman; thus he left a blight upon all the women of Buddhism.

The religion of Mohammed is even worse, for the very Heaven of the Koran is contingent upon the eternal degradation of womanhood.

The African woman is whipped and worked like a beast of burden, bought and sold and inherited like other property. Neither her childhood nor her motherhood is held sacred. She is the prey of the strong; her virtue is despised, her ruin encouraged. Her degradation is complete whether under animism or Mohammedanism, for the latter is "rotten to the core."

Thus we see that the major native religions of the Orient and Africa bring neither help nor hope to womanhood. Christian civilization has made of woman a person and a comrade for man; heathen civilization has made her a slave and a thing contemptible. How can a more effective blow be struck against the stronghold of this social oppression in heathendom than the entrance within its borders of Christian women dedicated to a life of mercy and healing; women free, firm, benign, intellectually developed, broad-minded, subservient to none, but ministering to all, the flower of a religion which counts them equal to men? Their professional service, great as that must be, may prove secondary in the end to the impression which they themselves must make upon the social scheme

into which they enter. Naturally, however, their
personal influence will work silently; its work will
be gradual, invisible, spiritual and so much the
more powerful in time.

Scope of work. The practical work of medical missionaries on the field is many-sided
and manifold, including dispensary and clinical
work; medical and surgical; the training of nurses;
instruction in regard to sanitation, cleanliness, nu-
trition; hospital work; professional training schools
and colleges for native women. All this is what our
women medical missionaries are performing today
at every station where they are found, but responsibility for those services is only half, the lesser
half, of the responsibility they carry. The healing
of the spirit is ever present as the supreme purpose, to be reached through the healing of the
body. This purpose will be considered under the
division of the subject next to follow. The remaining
question at this point is, Do women show themselves capable of holding their place in the Battalion of Life as it advances to the hand-to-hand
grapple with sin-sickness in heathendom? Have
they "made good"?

Let us glance through records of service past and
present, and quote, almost at random, a few names;
the plain, unvarnished facts will give us the most
eloquent answer.

Miss Hewlett of the Church of England Zenana
Missionary Society, who came to Amritsar, North
India, in 1879, was one of the small group of women
who undertook single-handed to carry on a medical
mission before it was possible to obtain a British

qualification in medicine. She founded St. Catherine's Hospital over which she presided for twenty-eight years and which in succeeding years furnished medical workers for all parts of India. Its influence is felt far and wide today, since it is a recruiting and training ground for Indian Christian nurses. Miss Hewlett was instrumental also in starting the Medical School for Women at Ludhiana.

A tiny city dispensary of two rooms was opened in the Mohammedan quarter of Amritsar, where, on the first day, only one woman timidly presented herself for treatment. The institution has expanded to a building two hundred and fifty-five feet in length, capable of holding forty-two patients, while altogether one hundred people live on the premises. Three large dispensaries are connected with it, the third being situated close to the Golden Temple, at a spot frequented by women who come to bathe in the Sacred Tank, and, therefore, peculiarly advantageous. A converts' school, a training home for nurses and compounders, a crèche, an industrial home for the blind, and a convalescent home for destitute women are some of the agencies grouped together around St. Catherine's.

As early as 1884 the care of the Maternity Hospital was committed to Miss Hewlett by the municipal authorities, since which time the systematic training of midwives has always been a most important and successful department of the work. Naturally, opportunities for reaching women in their own homes have multiplied, and zenana visitation has received a tremendous impetus. A large share in special ministry to the famine-stricken has been taken by the Amritsar workers, and during 1900 fifty widows and children from the Bhil country were received at St. Catherine's.

In this one home of healing, the devoted workers minister to as many as thirty-three thousand in the year, while upwards of three thousand visits are paid to patients in their homes. Who can gauge the result of such widespread seed-sowing and individual dealing with sin-sick souls as these figures represent?

Think next of that intrepid medical woman, Martha Sheldon, who, accompanied by her little band of workers, established herself in her "house of cloth" in Thibet, "the roof of the world," where her wonderful cures and successful treatment of cataracts opened the door for the Christ to enter into other women's hearts.

In his latest book on Thibet, Mr. Henry Savage Landor says, "At Sirka a Christian church of stone has arisen—the first one in British Thibet—the work of the untiring and self-sacrificing Miss Sheldon of America.". . . . Many lamas became her patients and only a few months before her death she went again over the lofty Lipu Pass—the entrance into Thibet, over seventeen thousand feet high—and over the Utla Pass, after traversing which the Lakes burst upon the traveler's vision. In her report for 1912 we find the following:

"Again medical work opened the way for me to spend two weeks in Thibet. I was called to Lake Manasarowar to operate for cataract upon women living near its monastery, and performed the operations in the stone house built for pilgrims and traders outside. Just before reaching the Lakes we saw the symmetrical Kailas Pahor Mountain. The snows had so melted as to cut a huge, black cross upon its white surface. The effect was wonderful.

"It seemed as if the Christ had gone before us, as indeed He has. I am reminded that fair, wooded Nepal and bleak, wind-swept Thibet lie almost wholly unevangelized. Right here in Bhot, which with Thibet is the tramping place and trading place of nations, there are indeed souls to conquer for Christ's Kingdom. As we walked slowly over the mountains up and down, I pondered whether I was living out of touch with the world in thus traveling so slowly in these days of lightning speed. I decided it all depended upon one's life work. Mine is to reach and to win the Bhotiyas and those allied to them to Christ. They travel with their great flocks of loaded sheep slowly. I, in traveling thus, came more in touch with them, so I content myself with a very humble work, in a very humble corner, in a very humble way."

Among the pioneer women medical missionaries we note the name of Dr. Ellen F. Mitchell. At the age of thirty she became an army nurse in the Civil War, serving three years in this capacity. In 1871 she graduated from the Women's Medical College in New York and in 1879, at the age of fifty years, sailed as a missionary to Moulmein, Burma. During twenty-two years of devoted service Dr. Mitchell returned her salary, in great part, to the treasury, and devoted all that she possessed, as all that she was, to her service of love and healing. Her

MISS EDITH BROWN, M.A., M.D.
Founder and Principal of the Woman's Christian Medical
College, Ludhiana, Punjab, North India

professional skill was regarded as marvelous, and she was affectionately styled "the little doctor" among the native people. Dr. Mitchell's cherished desire was to establish a maternity hospital and training school for nurses in Moulmein. This she did not live to do, but in 1917, sixteen years after her death, a site on a hill above the city was acquired by the Woman's Society represented by Dr. Mitchell, and a finely equipped maternity hospital is now in process of construction, to be known as the Ellen Mitchell Memorial Hospital and Training School for Nurses. Thus is rendered permanent the influence and work of the faithful pioneer woman who laid down her life in the service of the Great Physician.

These instances are given, not as exceptional, but as typical. Statistics and facts afford clear and abundant demonstration. Look up the records and read how, in her station at Kimpese on the Congo, Dr. Catherine Mabie in five months, besides devoting two or three hours a day to teaching in the training school, treated twelve thousand patients; how Dr. Benjamin in Nellore in five months treated four thousand, one hundred and forty-four women and children from every class, high and low, caste and outcaste, Mohammedans, heathen, and Christians; how Miss Gerow, assisting Dr. Benjamin during a scourge of cholera, also helped care for many of the missionaries who could not be cared for in their stations; how the Chinese hospitals, during the war between Japan and China, were carried on by two women whose names received honorable mention at the highest court; how Dr.

Mary Fulton for fifteen years worked and prayed for a women's and children's hospital in Canton and had not only the joy of seeing it established, but also a training school for nurses and a medical college for women, which are showing today results of high order.

What shall we say more? Time fails us to multiply these names as we might. Women have "made good" as medical missionaries. Further, it is imperative that they so do since, as we shall see clearly in the course of this study, *the fact remains that the male physician cannot reach the most needy cases of all and the very ones most inaccessible to other missionaries of either sex.*

IV. Ideals of the Battalion

We hear again the challenge to the Battalion of Life, not alone in the extent, nor yet in the needs of the sufferers, nor solely in the character of the service rendered—these, yes, all of them, but supremely comes the call in the potency of its idealism. Already above the tumult of the war comes that clarion note. Spiritual ideals have suddenly become realized on a tremendous scale. The Battalion of Life with its twofold message is uniquely adapted for the delicate, difficult work of implanting ideals, for the millions in non-Christian lands know only a loveless religion—an idealless religion. The ideals of the Battalion of Life are meaningless unless worked out in action, and men and women are called upon to enlist in this hour in numbers that they may carry on, not let drop, the revived idealism of compassion.

A twofold
gospel.

In its twofold message dwell the dominant ideals of the medical missionary enterprise; healing for the body, the love of Jesus Christ for the soul. Humanitarian and philanthropic service, noble as it is, does not constitute religion despite the strong tendency of the spirit of the age to declare that it does. "Many of us can remember the day," says an anonymous writer in the *Atlantic Monthly*, "when we were taught that we had immortal souls, to whose safeguarding thought and care and profound endeavor must go. The chief question was, 'Is it right or wrong?' The chief question today is, 'Is it sterilized?' Life, which used to be a brave flight between heaven and hell, has come to be a long and anxious tiptoeing between the microbe and the antiseptic."

The modern position so cleverly satirized in these sentences defines a very real temptation which comes to every scientific student of life, perhaps especially to the physician—the temptation to a materialistic interpretation of all things, a letting-go of those things which, being inward and spiritual, can be only spiritually discerned. To this temptation a woman, temperamentally, is less open than a man, hence the woman medical missionary is conspicuously adapted to the twofold ministry of healing with its religious implications and imperatives.

Qualifications.

Fitness for a place in the ranks of the Battalion of Life demands,—besides thorough technical training,—invincible faith, invincible hope, invincible love; added to these, a spirit of obedience to orders, courage, loyalty, self-denial, fortitude. Who can deny that these characteristics belong in full measure to woman? Who can doubt that she will hold through depths of darkness and degradation to the light of her divine ideals?

V. Review of the Battalion

We have seen that our Battalion of Life numbers today about one thousand qualified medical men and women missionaries, not including native doctors and native helpers or nurses. Not an imposing number in view of the Christian host of five hundred and fifty million of all creeds and complexions. The proportion of physicians in mission fields to those in the United States is as one to four thousand.

Pioneers. Precisely a century ago, in 1819, the first medical missionary, John Scudder, M.D., sailed for India, there to labor for six and thirty years. His son, Dr. H. M. Scudder, founded in Arcot, in 1850, the first regularly organized medical mission in India, with hospital and dispensary. In 1834 Dr. Peter Parker, a graduate of Yale University, was appointed a medical missionary and sailed at once for Canton, China. He is often described as the man who "opened China at the point of his lancet"; with little exaggeration this may be said, for Doctor Parker in 1839 began the training of the native Chinese in the practice of medicine and surgery, a circumstance which has contributed, in process of time, in substantial degree, to the breaking-down of the Chinese wall of prejudice and isolation.

In the year 1849, seventy years ago, the whole Battalion of Life consisted of forty men; but Dr.

Livingstone was in Africa, Dr. Hepburn in Japan,
Drs. Lockhart, Hobson and others in China. The
campaign was slow but steady. In 1864 Dr. David-
son (L.M.S.) wrote from the Island of Madagascar:
"Today I began building the hospital, the first in
the Island. It shall stand at Anàlakèly as a testimony
to our humanity, our science, and our Christianity."
In 1865 Dr. Elmslie (C.M.S.) wrote: "Today is
memorable in the history of the Kashmir Medical
Mission, from the fact that I opened my dispensary
this morning. . . . My small hospital" (started on
the doctor's verandah) "accommodates from four to
five patients." That humble hospital in due time
grew to be an extensive well-equipped institution,
where in a year thirty-eight thousand, five hundred
and seventy-three treatments were given and over
five hundred major operations performed.

When did women enter upon the work of medical
missions? By whom and under what influences were
the beginnings made?

Introductory. Mention should be made, in answer-
ing these questions, of an English-
woman, Mrs. Winter, wife of a missionary in India,
who, on her own impulse and under no auspices,
but the call of God and humanity, began in 1863
the labor of visitation of sick women and children
in Delhi, together with the administration of simple
medicine and nursing. From this beginning has come
St. Stephen's Hospital for Women and Children in
Delhi, with two important branches dedicated most
appropriately to Mrs. Winter, and carrying on a
great work among women and children. This interesting personal work cannot, however, be said to

have inaugurated medical mission work for women.

In her valuable study book *Western Women in Eastern Lands*, Helen B. Montgomery has given (pp. 124-131) a review of the early, operating causes which led the first regularly qualified Christian woman physician to enter heathendom for the practice of her profession and in so doing to found a medical mission. The impulse came, as Mrs. Montgomery tells us, from the missionaries on the field, for the men physicians found themselves cut off from access to secluded native women in sickness, while the women missionaries were handicapped by ignorance of the theory and practice of medicine. The "missionary medical closet" was a poor substitute for the living labor of the trained practitioner. In answer to appeals for "female missionaries who knew something of medical science," Mrs. Sarah G. Hale, of Philadelphia, organized in 1851 the "Ladies Medical Missionary Society," whose object was *"to aid the work of foreign missions by sending out young women qualified as physicians to minister to the wants of women in heathen lands."* In view of the date, marking a time when, as we have seen, women in medicine were looked upon with scorn and derision, as being wholly "out of their sphere," we must accord Mrs. Hale (who might, as editor of a ladies' "fashion magazine," have been expected to be on the popular side), the distinction of being a bold and valiant radical. But Mrs. Hale appealed, apparently, without response to the cautious and decorous circles of Philadelphia. Then, once more, the S.O.S. was sounded from the foreign field, this time not in vain.

The initiative* in this instance came from an
educated Hindu gentleman, Pundit Nund Kishore,
who knew the dreadful suffering of women in childbirth under the malpractice of ignorant native midwives. Under his influence a class of nine native
young women was opened at Naini Tal May 1, 1869,
a day worthy of everlasting remembrance in India.
The thrilling news came to this country to Mrs.
J. T. Gracey that four of these girls had successfully passed government examinations and had received their certificates in "Anatomy, Midwifery,
Pharmacy, and the management of minor surgical
cases." With the tidings came the appeal for a
thoroughly qualified missionary woman physician.
In response to this appeal inquiries were made at
the first of all American Women's Medical Schools,
that in Philadelphia, for a graduate ready and fitted
to go to India as the first enlisted woman soldier
in the Battalion of Life.

A candidate for this immortal honor appeared,—
Clara Swain, M.D., of Castile, New York. She was
sent out by the Woman's Foreign Missionary Society of the Methodist Episcopal Church, sailing
November third, 1869, reaching Bareilly January 2,
1870. There she commenced practice the following
morning. In less than three months she had formed
a class of native girls in the study of medicine; three
years later thirteen of them were granted certificates
to practice in all ordinary diseases. The need for a
hospital soon became urgent and the only eligible
site was some property joining the mission premises

---

* See *Women's Medical Work in Foreign Lands*, Mrs. J. T. Gracey.

owned by a Mohammedan, an opposer of Christianity, who lived some forty miles away. Dr. Swain with four other missionaries decided to appeal to him for the purchase of this property. To their embarrassment, he said, "Take it, take it," giving outright an estate of forty-two acres with a large brick house, two fine old wells, trees and a garden, worth at least fifteen thousand dollars. January 1, 1874, a new hospital was completed, the first for Oriental women, whose cost, including the remodeling of the house as a home and dispensary, was about eleven thousand dollars.* That year the number of Dr. Swain's patients reached three thousand. Her term of foreign service was twenty-seven years and every hour of every day was inspired by love of Christ and her fellow men.

In 1871 the Presbyterian women sent out their pioneer, Miss Sara C. Seward, niece of the Secretary of State, to Allahabad, India, where she died of cholera, in 1891. Her memorial is the beautiful Sara Seward Hospital, where twenty-four thousand, one hundred and forty-five patients were treated in 1909. In 1873 the Congregational Board sent out Dr. Sarah F. Norris of New Hampshire to Bombay. In less than three months she had prescribed for four hundred patients. All homes were open to her, Hindu, Parsi, Mohammedan, Christian, high caste, low caste, rich, or poor. More than fifteen thousand received religious instruction and treatment annually at her dispensary. To the Woman's Foreign Mis-

---

* For sketch of Dr. Swain's service in India see *Western Women in Eastern Lands*, by H. B. Montgomery, pp. 187-196, United Mission Study Series, 1910.

CHILDREN IN HOSPITAL WINTER GARMENTS
(wadded for warmth) on Steps of W. F. M. S.
Hospital, Tientsin
(By permission of the World Outlook)

sionary Society of the Methodist Episcopal Church belongs also the honor of sending out the first woman physician to China—Dr. Lucinda Coombs, of New York, appointed for Peking, in 1873; also the first fully trained physician to Korea, Dr. Meta Howard, in 1887; and the first to the Philippines, Dr. Anna J. Norton, in 1900. In 1879 Baptist women sent out as their pioneers Dr. Ellen F. Mitchell to Burma and Dr. Caroline H. Daniels to Swatow, China, and in 1881 Dr. Ida Faye to Nellore, India. Dr. Anna S. Kugler was sent to South India in 1883 by the Lutheran Church. In 1886 the Presbyterians sent to Korea Miss Ellers, a trained nurse who lacked but a little of being a fully trained physician. The pioneer Englishwoman was Dr. Fanny J. Butler, sent to India in 1880 by the Church of England Zenana Missionary Society.

Such, in brief, was the initial stage of Christian women's medical mission work for the women of heathen nations. Its development, method, and accomplishment in various countries will hereafter engage our attention.

"In the culture of the past, Thou, Christ, art the only modern. None felt with Thee the sympathy for man as man. They felt for man as Greek, as Jew, as Roman, but not as man— not as hopeless, friendless, landless. Thou hast gone down beneath all qualities, beneath beauty and virtue and fame. Thou hast broken the barriers of caste; Thou hast reached the last motive for charity—the right of hunger to bread. O Son of Man, Thou hast been before us. Thou hast outrun our Philanthropy; Thou hast anticipated our Benevolence; Thou hast forestalled our Charity; Thou hast modelled our Infirmaries; Thou hast planned our Orphanages; Thou hast sketched our Asylums; Thou hast devised our Houses of Refuge; Thou hast projected our Homes of Reform; Thou hast vindicated the claims of the returned convict; Thou hast asserted the sacredness of infant life; Thou hast given a hand to the climbing woman; Thou hast outstripped both Peter and John in the race to the ancient sepulchres of humanity; at the end of all our progress we have met Thee."

Rev. George Matheson, D.D.

"When among the mountains of Persia, in a part that no European had visited before, the few medicines I carried with me made a way for me everywhere to the hearts of the people.

" 'What do you do this for?' the people would ask me and I would reply: 'I do it for the love of Jesus, my Master and Lord.'

" 'You call Jesus your Master and Lord?' they would say, 'and we think the same about Mahomet. But we have no *Hakim* in the likeness of Jesus.'

"A *Hakim* in the likeness of Jesus! Was there ever before so beautiful a definition of the medical missionary?"

Isabella Bird Bishop.

OUTLINE OF CHAPTER II.

INDIA

1. *General Conditions.*

2. *Practice among Secluded Women, Zenana and Purdah.*

3. *Hospital, Dispensary and General Practice.*

4. *The Training of Native Women Physicians.*

5. *Impact of Woman's Medical Missionary Work upon the Social Fabric of India.*

CHAPTER II.

INDIA

"When I find a field too hard for a man I put in a woman."
Bishop Taylor.

INDIA preeminently among the countries which
come within the scope of our present study is possessed and governed by an alien race. For over a
century Great Britain has ruled India by right of
conquest, conquest made in the eighteenth century,
before the conscience of Christendom had condemned
the annexation of territory by military measures.
The inhabitants of India, then, are subject to Christian, not heathen, rule or *Raj*, to use the Indian
term; they enjoy enlightened justice and internal
peace in place of constant warfare,—the *Pax Britan-
nica.*

1. General Conditions

It would be natural, this being so, to look for
enlightened and progressive social conditions in
India, but it remains a land of paradox and mystery,
learned but uneducated, inert, impassive, apathetic,
fatalistic, in the main inveterately heathen still.
For this condition not Great Britain, but the very
nature of things is responsible. The British Raj,
which grants the Christian missionary freedom and

protection in his work and worship, must of necessity grant like freedom and protection to the native
people in the practices of their ethnic religions,
however perverse and idolatrous.

Social character-   The average Hindu of today wears
istics.   the same fashion of raiment that he
did in the time of Moses; he ploughs, it might almost
be said, with the same plough, lives in the same hut,
made of mud and thatched with straw that he did
then, he earns, as he did then, his penny a day; he
eats the same grain, ground with the same millstones, and he has been hungry, as some one has
said, for thirty centuries, it never having occurred
to him that he had any claim to be filled. In whatever caste he was born he and his sons and his sons'
sons remain, whatever handicaps it entails. Caste,
the inflexible division of all men and women according to the condition or avocation of their ancestors,
determines everything from the cradle to the grave.
The Hindu is patient; he is not progressive. He has
the virtues and the vices common to subject peoples,
and that he manifests these in striking degree is to
be expected, for the Hindus have been a subject
people for over a thousand years.

Brahmanism.   Truly, India is a land of mystery
and paradox. The learned Brahman
will recite with fervor a noble Vedic hymn, familiar
from time immemorial, in praise of the one and only
God; will depart then to make his offering to a
three-headed goddess, gaudy in red paint, or to the
elephant-headed Ganesa, the unspeakable Linga,
the licentious Krishna, or some other of the thirty-
three million divinities in the Brahmanic system.

He combines the subtlest mystical philosophy with the grossest forms of idolatry and licentiousness.

Status of women. All Hindu sects agree upon two points: the sanctity of the cow and the depravity of woman. A Brahman suspends reading the Veda if a woman comes in sight; her ear is too impure to hear what he, no matter how vile, may read. There are two ways by which woman in India can vindicate her existence; the first is by bearing a son. Hence child marriage, with its train of terrible woes. The second is by becoming "a bride of the gods." This signifies entering the Temple Service and debasement unutterable.

Because of the unchangeable enactment of the code of Manu, and because of its doctrine that women are inherently bent upon evil, evil only, and that continually, Hindus, all but the lower class, seclude their women rigorously. The apartments used for this darkened and muffled existence are known as the zenana. The law of Manu declares: "A woman is not allowed to go out of the house without the consent of her husband; she may not laugh without a veil over her face or look out of a door or a window."

Islam. For a thousand years, until superseded by the British Raj, the major part of India was subject, more or less solidly, to Moslem rule. The last Mohammedan Mughal surrendered to the British in 1857, after the fall of Delhi, and with his downfall and death the political power of Islam in India ended. But today one-third of all the followers of the prophet in the world are found in India, about sixty million. The Moslem's estimate of women is not higher than that of the Hindu, hence the harem, where the head of the house, usually polygamous, segregates and secludes the women of his household behind the purdah. There are in India forty million secluded women.

Moslem and Hindu women alike, under native conditions, are destitute of even rudimentary education. At the present time, in India only one woman in a hundred can read and write. This is according to the unchanging temper and policy of the land. The lives of these secluded women are vacant and trivial beyond description; often vicious, always on a low plane,—mentally, morally, and physically they are subnormal. The appeal of their darkened, depressed, and suffering condition to the heart of Christian womanhood is irresistible; affecting, indeed, is their readiness to respond to word and touch of sympathy and aid.

Buddhism. Three great religions have gained sway in India. We have spoken of the place of women under Brahmanism and Mohammedanism, to this day in full force. The third, Buddhism, originating in Northern India in the sixth century, B. C., was driven out of the peninsula about 900 A.D., but is still all-powerful in Ceylon, where it numbers two million five hundred thousand adherents, and in Burma, where they exceed in number ten million. Both Ceylon and Burma belong to British India. The women of Burma are described as the most emancipated in Asia. While Buddhism does not seclude its women and does not support the pernicious system of caste, the education of women is neglected; social conditions are low; superstition, idolatry, and dense ignorance still prevail. Above all things the religion of Buddha is fatalistic. *Karma,* the inflexible law of cause and effect in human life, is the universal watchword of Buddhism, as *Kismet,* "destiny," is that of the follower of Islam, and *Maya,* "all is illusion," of the Hindu.

India is the classic land of foreign missions. First of heathen lands to be entered by missionaries, it is crowded with heroic names and heroic deeds. Rich with memories of our own saints and martyrs, it is hallowed ground, potent in its appeal to our sympathy, our imagination, and to our loyalty to our dead who have died to make it free.

India classic ground for missions. From the legendary visit of the Apostle Thomas in the first century to the present day, India has not been left without witness, however feeble or imperfect, for the Christian religion. With the landing of William Carey in Calcutta, in November, 1793, the epoch of the modern Protestant enterprise of evangelization began. This was a century and a quarter ago. In 1850, medical missions were established in form. This was three-quarters of a century ago. In 1870, with the entrance of Clara Swain, M.D., upon her work, woman's medical missions for the women of India began in form. This was half a century ago.

In studying the work accomplished in India proper in these fifty years by the several methods open to them, it should be borne ever in mind that our missionaries constantly contend with the inflexible barriers of the seclusion of women, of caste, of superstition and of dense ignorance.

2. Practice among Secluded Women,
Zenana and Purdah

The earliest method of evangelizing higher caste Indian women was known as zenana work, meaning the personal religious visits of women missionaries to secluded women. From the conditions discovered in these visits came the first call for medical missionary women.

In 1870, her first year in India, Dr. Swain was called to visit sixteen different zenanas; this was the sharp point of the entering wedge. Her service to the wife of the Rajah of Rajputana at Khetri opened the way for her to enter one of the great native states, there to practice her Christian ministry of healing for seventeen years.

The exact counterpart of the zenana or the harem is unknown in western lands. The system and the influences going out from it are the cause of much of the disease common among women and children. It is impossible adequately to picture it, even to imagination, for in the minds of western women there is no standard of comparison. The principles of inferiority and seclusion ordained by the ethnic religions have filtered down through every grade of the social strata.

What is a zenana? is a question often asked. Briefly, it is that portion of an Indian gentleman's house set apart for the women. Imagination is apt to invest such a place with the gorgeous surroundings which are usually associated with Indian wealth and rank. But the reality is, in most cases, dull and prosaic in the extreme. Instead of a mansion, think of a mud building, bare and uninviting, probably the darkest and dirtiest part of the establishment. Do not imagine that the inmates are attired with Oriental magnificence. They are poorly and plainly clad; they sit on the floor, and the whole place is more suggestive of the hopeless seclusion of the prison than the social sunshine of the home. In these dens, forty millions of the women in India are kept. They have none of the joys of family life, for the women never gather with husband and children. To women in the zenana, life is without an inspiring purpose; it sinks to drudgery worse than that of a treadmill.

Woe betide the women when they become sick! Then, of all times, we should expect a little kindly attention to be shown them. But the sufferers are relegated to some damp chamber, where they are left alone, often with no ministries of loving hands to soothe and comfort their last hours. Is not the dull and cheerless existence of such women a living death? Many a zenana would remain forever closed, even against the woman missionary, if it were not for the medical mission. Where no one else can gain access medical women are freely admitted and much good work is quietly and unostentatiously accomplished in the name of the Great Physician.

A case was reported by a medical woman in North India which illustrates the tenacity of these social laws, even among those who have received an English education and mixed freely with English people. She writes as follows:

"The house surgeon of a government hospital, a clever man and a Sikh by birth and religion, came to me one morning in great distress. He said his daughter-in-law, a young girl of barely sixteen, was dangerously ill and he could do nothing for her, as he must not see her face nor touch her further than to feel her pulse. The girl was living in the house with the husband's parents and her father-in-law had never seen her face all the time she was there. . . . . No English father-in-law, however, could have been more distressed than this man was."

Hysteria.   "It must not be thought that this se-clusion is merely a species of slavery enforced on the women by the men. Whatever its origin, it is now most tenaciously kept up by the women themselves as a badge of respectability, even when the men of the household, their own prejudices weakened by education, would gladly call a doctor. As matters stand, it is true to say that, for the most part, the women in these zenanas may suffer or may die, but no man doctor will ever be called in to see them. Illustrations have already been given of some of the horrors which go on in the name of medical treatment at the hands of some of their ignorant attendants. The very confined life they lead predisposes the women to many kinds of ail-ments, and hysteria in all its forms is rife. It can easily be understood that the elusive nature of the symptoms is just what lends itself to the prevalent belief in evil spirits as the cause of all disease. As a rule, the unfortunate patient herself is as firmly convinced of being under Satanic influence as any of the household. This leaves an open door for the impostures of the wizard and the quack doctor and even if the remedies employed by the latter are less violent and less injurious than those of the wizard, the condition of the confirmed hysteric is pitiable in the extreme. She generally goes from bad to worse, until the family is weary of her and kindness and misplaced pity turn to active brutality."

Native treatments. Native treatments, for which the Hindus will pay vastly more than they would pay for Western medicine, consist of the wearing of a bit of sacred wood made into a bracelet or necklace, armlet or toelet; or it may be a verse from the Koran, or a verse copied from the sacred writings, placed in a container and worn round the neck as a charm; or it may be placed in the turban or tied up in the corner of the one-piece garment worn by men and women. Sometimes the word Allah has been written on a plate a number of times with India ink and washed off. This water is then given to the patient to drink for a raging fever, or an indolent ulcer, or a broken bone. When powders are given, often the inquiry is made as to whether the paper, too, should be eaten.

Dr. Staley describes a typical form of treatment meted out to the sick in the zenanas. "I found a woman," she wrote, "delirious with fever after childbirth. She was propped up in a sitting posture on a filthy bed in a dark room, and beside her crouched two old crones, one on each side. Grasping her hair in their long, lean hands they occupied themselves in violently shaking her head backwards and forwards with all their might and main, tearing out handfuls of hair in their vigorous efforts. As one got exhausted the other relieved her. This procedure was intended to evict the evil spirit with which they imagined the poor creature to be possessed. All but the back part of her hair had been pulled out, and, moreover, she was evidently starved, as she swallowed some milk with great avidity. The nurse who was with me fetched a litter and we had her carried promptly to the hospital, explaining carefully to the men of the family that it was merely to allow the poor woman to die in peace and comfort, out of reach of their fiendish cruelty."

Maternity work. At every turn of woman's medical work the physician is confronted by the ever-present, hideous, one had almost said murderous, customs which have to do with maternity practices. Every doctor and nurse should have special preparation for this; indeed, it is not too much to say that every woman missionary should have such preparation. A practicing English physician was at home from India on furlough. A well-known Edinburgh obstetrician inquired if he had seen much midwifery practice in India. He replied, "We had been seven years in practice before we were called to a confinement case, and then it was a cow. No department of medical practice is so unequally distributed among us. On the other hand, among many, if not all, of our women doctors, midwifery is the most important part of their work and perhaps their greatest opportunity." (*Indian Medical Missionary Magazine.*)

3. Hospital and Dispensary Practice

The conditions already outlined give rise to a vast amount of avoidable illness and create an obvious need for suitable hospitals. The inaccessibility of caste calls loudly and imperatively for the zenana hospital. Here women are accorded similar protection to that to which they are accustomed, and gradually prepared for the new life that awaits their emancipation. They see here a new and strange religion lived before their eyes. There are now in India one hundred and eighty mission hospitals and less than four hundred dispensaries. The number of foreign women physicians on the field is given in *World Statistics of Christian Missions*, latest edition, as one hundred and fifty-nine.

Hospitals.   A typical women's hospital on a small scale in Northern India may be sketched; it is built of sun-dried bricks, plastered with mud, at a cost of Rs.500.* It contains one large ward and four small ones, holding altogether fourteen beds. This building stands in a courtyard of its own, quite separate from the dispensary courtyard, which contains the operating, consulting, drugstore rooms and dispensary, as well as the outpatients' waiting room. The hospital wards have clean, red brick floors, freshly whitewashed walls, bright with illuminated texts in Hindustani and other dialects. The bedsteads are the native wooden frames, *nawar*†-strung, made by industrial classes; sheets and bedding are of coarse weave, but of immaculate cleanness as is everything in the place. This feature is no less striking in its novelty to the wealthy patient than to the poor. The former have more jewels than the latter, but no less undisturbed

---

* A rupee is about fifty cents.   † Webbing.

dirt in all their belongings. The patients, on being brought into the hospital, are forcibly impressed first with this cleanness, then with the absolute truthfulness and the genuine love and interest shown them by doctor, nurses, and attendants.

Clinical Christianity.   In the dispensary the nurse provides each newcomer with a metal number to indicate her turn. If the poorest outcaste receives the first number, she is the first to receive attention. A white-clad Bible woman gives each sufferer a few words of teaching regarding the compassionate Christ and His good news of life and light, as the shifting company passes to the consulting room, thence to the door of the drug room for medicine or to receive minor surgical treatment, then, passing out, scatters each to his or her own place. Thus the days go on, three hundred and sixty-five in the year, through dry season and rainy season, through plague and cholera; the doors are always open, the doctor is always ready to listen and to minister to the piteous multitude in body and in mind.

The hospital here described is a small and humble beginning with a noble future before it, but there are many women's mission hospitals throughout India of larger proportions, built of stone, beautiful in their architecture, surrounded with the graceful, distinctive Indian colonnades, set amid tropical gardens and grassy lawns. Such a hospital has its separate isolation building, substantial nurses' home, its detached bungalow for the American staff, its large and small wards, all high and airy, its well-equipped operating, lying-in, and sterilizing rooms; above all, it serves its purpose in the treatment of

RESIDENT STAFF, DAVID GREGG HOSPITAL,
HACKETT MEDICAL COLLEGE,
CANTON, CHINA
(By permission of the Foreign Missions Library)

NATIVE AMBULANCE IN CHINA
In which most of our severely wounded and cases unable
to walk are brought

thousands of suffering women and children each year.

Here is a snap-shot of the daily round and common task of a typical hospital in South India, as given by Frances Jeffery. "Separated only by a low wall from one of Madura's busiest thoroughfares, the American Mission Hospital for Women stands with doors ever open to the sick and distressed women and children of that country. Dr. Harriet E. Parker, our representative in the field of action, is a frail little woman and to meet her, after hearing on all sides of the tremendous work she is doing, simply makes the romantic struggle seem all the more wonderful. It makes us feel the strength that must come from a deep-rooted faith in the Divine Healer. Like all doctors, Dr. Parker works while others sleep.

"Gentle in her manner, she not only inspires confidence in her patients, but also wins their love and the love of her subordinates. In spite of poor equipment and insufficient help, she leads her assistants with such enthusiasm and unselfishness that they serve her loyally and efficiently. Until recently, when Dr. Scott, from America, and Miss Ruth Heath, a trained nurse from England, came to aid Dr. Parker, she has carried her burdens with only the help of the Indian nurses and compounders.

"Half an hour, an hour even, before the dispensary doors are opened to the eager people outside, the doctor makes her morning visit to the wards. From cot to cot she goes, giving kindly counsel as well as medical advice to the patients: to the silk weaver's wife who must have an operation and

thinks it very hard that only two from the large
number of friends and relatives who escorted her
hither may remain; to the low-caste girl who nearly
went blind from 'country sore eyes'; and to the
young Brahman woman whose interest in the Bible
brought her in touch with the woman who knew
where she might find relief for her pain.

"When the doors are opened at eight o'clock the
doctor is ready to receive her visitors, a variegated
assembly of women and children, some of whom
have ridden or walked many a weary mile to consult
the Doctor-lady. There are usually so many waiting
to see her that numbers are given out by one of the
nurses, so that all may go in their turn. Each patient
receives from the Doctor some prescription which
is forwarded to the drug room, and there, later, the
women go to reach out their hands for the much-
coveted medicine. As few of the woman-kind of
India are able to read, the bottles are decorated with
pieces of paper so notched as to show the number
and size of the doses to be taken. There is another worker in the waiting-room, besides the
nurses and attendants, the Bible woman, who takes
this opportunity to talk to the waiting women of
the Christ and of the religion that brings happiness
to its believers."

Dr. Parker's work is not confined to the hospital.
She has many calls to go into the homes of the native women in and about Madura. The Hindu
woman still resents the entrance of a man doctor
into her home for attendance in illness, and, as Dr.
Parker has been until recently the only woman
physician in Madura, and indeed in the whole dis-

trict embraced by the Madura Mission, her ability is constantly being pressed into service. In this country a doctor would think it more than sufficient to supervise a hospital, looking after the training of the nurses and compounders, without doing any service outside of the hospital. And well might Dr. Parker, since in one ward of the hospital alone, the obstetrical ward, there were one hundred and seventy-six cases during this last year, many of them neglected and desperate cases. All doctors know what this means as to anxiety, hours of hard work, skill, and every resource of instruments and delicate handling.

Her hospital work is a night and day task, and yet she is never too busy or too tired to answer a call of distress and emergency, even if it means a thirty-mile Jutka ride without food and without sleep.

Usually the missionary in charge of the station, to which her trip leads her, facilitates her work by sending out word of her arrival through the village catechists, thus having all in readiness for her coming. Perhaps through some woman who has been cured in her hospital, her fame has spread before her and the lame and the diseased come for miles to the village appointed for her visit, to be examined and to receive the healing medicine. Often there are cases of prolonged or desperate character and Dr. Parker usually prevails upon these to return with her to the hospital where, under the special care there given, they may recover.

What an opening this makes for Christianity!

During a recent year there were one thousand and

eighty-one in-patients and thirteen thousand seven hundred and forty-nine out-patients; total treatments forty-seven thousand eight hundred and twenty-three. Of this number one hundred and ninety-three were maternity cases, requiring ninety-three obstetrical operations. Total operations one thousand four hundred and seven.

Miss Ruth C. Heath, trained nurse, writes: "I confess I am a little tired; it is over ten weeks since I had one whole night in my bed! and the worst of it is Dr. Parker is tired, too; but we both keep at it and daily strength is always given to meet the day's work. Apart from my hospital work I find in adding up my 'out calls' for this year (1916) that they number nine hundred and seventy-seven. This in itself means quite a fair amount of time and work."

Dispensaries. An additional measure for providing medical aid is that of branch dispensaries. Unfortunately, the hospital staff is not usually large enough to permit of doing this work. Every hospital should have two or more such branches with a sufficient staff to make an alternating service possible. In this way what is done at the centre may be, in a measure, duplicated, and many sufferers may be helped who are too far away, too indifferent, or too fatalistic to come to the hospital. They frequently ask for medicine in the form of powders, fearing that the liquid used in the mixture may be water, drinking which would cause them to lose caste or, perhaps, unconsciously coerce them to become Christians and hence outcasts. In this branch work the practical difficulty lies in being unable to see the patients often enough to do them any good. If no visible result occurs within a few hours, they immediately seek a new doctor. The astonishingly common sore eyes need constant attention and cleanliness, instead of the unwashed garment so convenient to apply and so contaminating. If in the case of a child the application of the lotion causes pain, the parents will not use it, for the one unpardonable sin is to allow infants to cry. When they cry the remedy is the convenient opium which is freely used throughout the country.

According to the last available statistics there were over four million treatments given during the last year. Hardly one of these patients left these hospitals and dispensaries without receiving a spiritual message, without seeing Christianity thus commend itself in blessing and power to the people of the land. Not one of them but could truthfully say, "We have no such thing in our religion." Among the thinking ones would also start the query, "Why this difference?" and the interrogation point would trace a path from Vishnu to Christ.

Sanitation. The strongest barrier against sanitation and cleanliness in India is the inflexible combination of ignorance and superstition.

The pious Hindu believes that the Ganges river rises from the nail of the large toe of Vishnu's left foot, then reissues from the moon and that the nymphs of heaven, by sporting in the water, have imparted to it life-giving power. He believes that any man who dies on the banks of that river is sure of Heaven, and that the sacred stream, desired, seen, touched, bathed in, sanctifies all being. It is impossible that such a faith can long survive the teaching of modern astronomy and geography, physiology and hygiene. Chemistry and bacteriology are making rubbish of a good deal of hoary and venerated idolatry. The evangel has many voices, science is one of them.

India has always been noted for its neglect not only of every hygienic precaution, but, in certain respects, of the simple decencies of living. Fresh air is more feared than snakes; squalor defies description. Missions, of course, have had little to do officially with the establishment and enforcement of modern sanitary regulations. The British Government is discharging this gigantic task as far and as fast as the serious difficulties allow. Missionaries, however, have much to do in preparing the people to welcome and respond to the efforts of the Government in this direction. It is the ignorant and bigoted children of superstition, the thronging pilgrims, the fanatical devotees, the slaves of custom, the men and women whose lives are stagnant and whose outlook has no gleam of better things, who are intractable and immovable.

When a deadly visitation, like the plague, appears in the midst of the people, they fly with offerings to their gods, disregarding the matter-of-fact administrator who endeavors to indoctrinate them with the laws of hygiene, and offers them disinfectants and other preventives. "It is the will of the gods," or "What is written on our foreheads will come to pass," is the response. To face and fight the trouble appears to the natives impious; all that they care to do is to petition their gods to stay the pest destroying them. Sentiments like these stand against sanitation, the people rejecting the saving hand, and, worse still, turning at times fiercely on their rescuers.

Their characteristic fatalism is well illustrated by the following conversation between an official and a Mohammedan:

Question: What is the death rate per thousand in your principal city?

Answer: It is the will of Allah that all should die. Some die young, some old.

Question: What is the annual number of births?

Answer: We do not know. God alone can say.

Question: Are the supplies of drinking water sufficient and of good quality?

Answer: From the remotest time no one has ever died of thirst.

Question: General remarks on the hygienic conditions in your city.

Answer: Since Allah sent us Mohammed, His Prophet, to purge the world by fire and sword, there has been a vast improvement, but there still remains much to do. Everywhere is opportunity to help and reform, and now, my lamb of the West, cease your questioning which can do no good, either to you or to any one else. Man should not bother himself about matters which concern only God. *Salem Aleikum.*

Epidemics. Little wonder that in India epidemics of plague and cholera are so frequent as to attract scant notice in the outside world. The Battalion of Life is hard at work fighting where it can the conditions which inevitably breed disease, but it is slow work contending against the prejudices of forty centuries.

But there are signs of cheer. "Severe epidemics are often the cause of apostasies among weak Christians. But fresh from passing through a widespread outbreak of cholera during the last rains," so says a medical missionary, "I can testify to the way in which efficient medical aid to our people in their distress and danger may make what might have been an occasion of falling a very sacrament of grace, drawing out all that was best in the simple, child-like faith which some are apt to despise in these, Christ's little ones."

Writing of plague conditions at Ahmednagar, Dr. Ruth Hume describes the invincible unwillingness of the people to submit to inoculation. "It is passing strange," she says, "to see how people refuse and put off and evade inoculation, which is given them absolutely freely by the Government. . . . I have not done as many as some of the other inoculators, only between twenty-seven hundred and twenty-eight hundred thus far. But I have had one privilege which some of the others lack, for I am not only a doctor but a woman, so I was asked to go to selected places in the city to which the purdah Mohammedan women could conveniently come. . . Today, October tenth, the day's plague figures are one thousand, fifty-five cases and seven hundred and ten deaths. And now cholera can be added to our almost necessary preventive treatments here. . . . Our nurses and staff have done splendidly handling the extra work made by plague patients, orphan babies, and inoculation."

The village
clinic.

Aside from home visiting the medical missionary has an important task in her regular touring through outlying villages. When her coming is expected the Christian preacher or teacher of each village gathers in the school house or sometimes under a tree by the wayside those who are sick and suffering. The doctor with her attendant nurse drives up, her medicine chest with her, and the work proceeds swiftly but systematically, fifty or sixty being cared for at each place visited, and at each the good seed of the Word being sown. Such a day's work may mean for the doctor fourteen hours of intense application, forty-six miles of travel, and three hundred patients treated.

4. Training Schools for Native Nurses and Physicians

School for
nurses.

There stands today in Guntur in Madras Presidency a large, well-equipped Lutheran hospital for women. It was formally opened for patients in 1898. As one enters the precincts of the hospital there is seen, at the right of the driveway, a picturesque, cloistered, two-story edifice, built of rough stone and brick. This is the nurses' home and training school for native women, model and type of what every medical mission in India requires. The first class of nurses in this school was graduated in 1901. Diplomas are granted in sick-nursing, compounding, and midwifery and those who have received them are proving themselves a power for good. Of prime importance for India is the need for trained midwives, the native *daie*, when untrained, proving themselves a menace to life by their cruel superstitions and ignorant malpractices. The unnecessary sacrifice of infant and mother life by this means is nothing less than appalling. Any fascination which Indian religious systems may have for Western minds disappears when the outworking of them is seen in the supreme crisis of maternity. The little girl who, at the age of twelve, must undergo the ordeal of childbirth, should at least have the chance for her life which is given by intelligent nursing.

Great as is the need for trained native nurses, the need for trained native women doctors is greater. Indeed, here is the main point on which the future of the enterprise which we are studying rests. Obviously, it is impossible for foreign women fully to supply the needs of India's suffering and neglected millions. Nor would it be according to the counsels of wisdom that this should be attempted. As rapidly as possible the Indian people should come to their own aid, should learn to stand on their own feet, should emerge from the dependent and helpless class. It is the purpose of our societies to help them to help themselves.

A glance at the preceding chapter will show us that under the heading Review of the Battalion, we found that the first strong, definite call for women medical missionaries had its origin in the formation, at the instance of a Hindu gentleman, of a class of native girls to study medicine. This was at Naini Tal, in May, 1869. Let it be kept in mind, then, that India first lifted her own voice for her own release from the cruel bonds which bound her.

Let us firmly believe that the seed of self-help, small and weak though it was, shall, in the end, bring forth abundant fruit after its kind.

Schools of medicine. There exist in India at the present time four important schools of medicine for women: one at Agra, one at Delhi, one at Ludhiana, a fourth in Vellore. The two first named are in the Northwest Provinces; Ludhiana in the Punjab, North India; Vellore in Madras Presidency, South India. The Agra Medical School belongs to the "Dufferin Scheme," a "National Association for supplying Female Medical aid to the Women of India," founded at the instance of Queen Victoria in 1886. While it is under government control, it is interesting to know that the Christian community has supplied most of the female candidates for the degree of sub-assistant surgeon in this school and that regular Bible classes are carried on among them. Out of sixty female students at a given time at Agra fifty were Christian girls. In 1898, the Lady Dufferin Association reported two hundred and forty female students under its charge in different medical schools and colleges. Wholly admirable as is this government-controlled enterprise, particular study of it, as of the Lady Hardinge school at Delhi, does not come within our present brief survey, otherwise than by sympathetic recognition.

There are but two expressly missionary schools of medicine for women in India, those at Ludhiana and at Vellore. These will be considered in Chapter VI.

5. Impact of Woman's Medical Missionary Work upon the Social Fabric of India

"The one great curse of our country is the uneducated mother and the illiterate wife," said an Indian lady of distinction in a public meeting at Bombay; "We are left to rot and waste in the darkness of ignorance and narrow prejudice. Lead us out from this 'Black Hole' and restore us to free air and the light of knowledge."

Object lessons. The women of Christian America can respond to this appeal in no more effective way than by sending fresh recruits to the body of medical missionaries ministering to the women thus described. Too ignorant to read of better ways, object lessons are the only method which pierces into the darkened mind and stimulates the native women to imitation. They see fundamentals without knowing it. They see the windows open, which in itself is a novelty; they see heads uncovered, which is never dreamed of at home in sickness or at night; they see even babies taking the fresh air cure and no demons carrying them off; they see ulcers, not little ones, but ample ones covering the whole foot or the leg, gradually changing to healthy tissue and no hot iron has been applied, nor filthy cow-dung poultice used; they see loving, tender, patient service such as they have never received in their lives before. In the very hospital building they see a memorial to some sainted woman, when woman, according to the teaching of their priests and their sacred books, has been held forever accursed. They see happy, healthy children coming out of suffering, weakness, and misery; they see even girls loved and cared for; they see those of their own country trained to be alert, active, effective in the same loving service, and they marvel.

"All I learn here," said a Mohammedan woman in a missionary hospital, "is of love. We hear no mention of love in our religion." Another, the wife of a highly educated Mohammedan gentleman, herself an eloquent testimony of what liberated womanhood may be in India, and a frequent visitor to a missionary hospital, said, "I never come here that I don't go away feeling rebuked that you do so much for our people and we do nothing." A prominent Mohammedan testifies: "It is these medical missionaries who are winning the hearts of our people. We, too, must build hospitals and care for the sick and the dying if we wish to keep our religion alive." With open eyes seeing all these things their hearts are made tender, very much as they were in the days of old when the Christ gave us the example, and as of old they are amazed.

A missionary in South India tells of an old woman who bitterly opposed the mission and tried to dissuade her relatives from attending the dispensary. Later she was attacked by a painful carbuncle on her knee. At last, receiving no help at home, she hobbled in pain to the mission hospital. Her experience at the hospital transformed her into a loyal friend of the mission, and day by day she may be heard exhorting the patients to trust the mission workers. "I was against them once," she tells them, "but now that I know what love means, they are my parents and I am their child. Caste? What is caste? I believe in the goodness they show, that is their caste."

"What's the matter with you?" says bed No. 1, contentedly. "My husband became angry with me, because the meal wasn't ready when he came home and he cut my face. The Doctor Miss Sahib has mended me, she has done what my own mother would not do." Said another in reply to the question, "The cow horned my arm, but until I got pneumonia I couldn't stop milking or making bread for the father of my children, even if it was broken. The hospital is my *Mabap* (mother-father)."

"What care would you get at home?" chimed in another who had been burning up with fever. "Oh! I would be out in the deserted part of the woman's quarters. It would be a wonderful thing if any one would pass me a cup of water," she replied. From another bed, a young wife of sixteen spoke of having been ill with abscesses. "One broiling day," she said, "I had fainted with thirst. The midwives had neglected me all through the night and, thinking I was dying, they threw me from the cord bed to the floor and dragged me down the steep stone staircase to the lowest floor where I was lying, next to the evil-smelling dust bin, ready for removal by the carriers of the dead, when the Doctor Miss Sahib found me and brought me here. She is my mother and I am her child."

The best part of it is that this deeper success does not depend upon the cure of the physical ills. Let us listen to this eloquent incident:

"The lady doctor* was out in camp some twelve miles from her station in South India. All day long a stream of suffering women and children sought her at the door of her tent and all day long they received her skilled and loving attention. In the evening, when the sun was setting, and she had seen the last of her patients for the day, she began to pack up her gloves and instruments preparatory to returning home in the cool of the night. Looking up she saw four men carrying a burden toward her little tent and waited to see what new claim on her attention this might be. Presently, they laid at her feet an outcaste man, the son of one of the bearers, in the grip of the cholera. What was she to do? I have no need to tell you what she did; love dictated that, and you have already seen what happened. Putting away all thought of returning home, she turned to this poor outcaste stranger to see if by any means she might save his life. All night long the woman doctor fought death in an unequal combat. All night long there was no ministry so repulsive but love held it. And all night long there was no service so lowly that love did not stoop to it. In the dawn he died, and as the morning broadened into sunrise the respectable Hindoos of the village, the men whose women and children she had been seeking to comfort and to heal during the whole of the preceding day, came out from their homes, and saw what had taken place. They spurned the doctor, because, having touched their women folk she had

* Contributed by the Rev. W. Goudie to *L.M.S. Chronicle*, February, 1914. See also *Yarns on Heroes of India*, p. 69.

also touched the filthy body of an outcaste man. They declared that never again should she be welcomed in their village or allowed to touch their people. Even the father of the dead man lifted up the corpse of his son and carried it away without so much as saying 'Thank you.' The woman doctor was left to make her way home over twelve miles of roadless country with weary limbs and aching head and a heart deeply wounded, for she said, 'I thought to have opened the door of usefulness, but I seemed to close one and to have wasted my night's labor.'

"But in six months the family of the dead man, the man whom she had sought to cure, were at the feet of her brother the missionary, pleading to be taken under his care and taught with a view to entering the Christian Church.

"'Why have you come?' said he, not unnaturally; to which they replied, 'We have come because we have seen what love can do. We never knew till then what love was. You thought that we did not care, because we did not speak, but our hearts were too full for speech. We want to belong to you.'

"The result was that in a short time the missionary in charge of the station was able to baptize a thousand people in that village and a little later could report that that new congregation had provided twelve Christian workers, evangelists, teachers and Bible women."

NURSES IN MARGARET WILLIAMSON HOSPITAL

MARGARET WILLIAMSON HOSPITAL,
SHANGHAI, CHINA
(By permission of the Woman's Union Missionary Society)

OUTLINE OF CHAPTER III.

CHINA

CHAPTER III.

"Send us more missionaries, especially doctors."
Li Hung Chang.

CHINA is the land of possibilities, undeveloped, but unbounded. She is a land of mighty reserve power, but this power, like that of her physical resources, her enormous supply of mineral deposits, has remained dormant. She is a sleeping, but not a dead giant. Napoleon at St. Helena said, "When China is moved it will change the face of the globe."

1. Comparison of China with India

A superficial comparison of the social state of China with that of India might suggest a close parallel. Both have dense and enormous populations. In both countries poverty reaches the lowest depth. Both are deeply tainted with conditions fatal to human health and life, conditions induced by age-long ignorance of public and private cleanliness and hygiene, hence both are cursed with leprosy, cholera, bubonic plague, loathsome diseases of the skin and eyes. In both the masses of the population are illiterate. Both are, in religion, idolatrous and priest-ridden. In both, women are secluded and oppressed as inferiors, miserably handicapped in the race of life. Alike in India and China the native treatment of disease is desperately evil, being controlled by gross superstition and ignorance.

The resemblance, obvious, but going not at all below the surface, fades the moment we recognize certain fundamental facts. While India shows the enervation of a tropical land, China has the energy of a colder climate, and does not bear the marks of a subject nation. The Chinese retain an independence, firmness of fibre, a vigor and a native intelligence in strong contrast to the languid apathy of an exhausted people like the Hindus. The seclusion and oppression of women in China does not rest upon the rock-foundation of an unchangeable religious code; it is a custom and a custom which has always been in some degree flexible. The women of China, though counted inferior, are by no means decadent or passive. Again, India staggers painfully along the path of progress under her paralyzing burden of caste. The Chinese have no similar handicap; they are the most democratic of people. The only aristocracy is that of learning.

Again, idolatry, while prevalent in China, is less gross, unclean, and multiform than in India and is destitute of the corruption of lascivious rites such as prevail in goddess-worship in certain Hindu sects, or of customs akin to that of the dedication of young girls to the service of the Temple.

A strong point of promise for China's future is found in her native inventive intelligence in the past. China invented, long centuries ago, gunpowder, block-printing, banknotes, porcelain, the compass and many other devices commonly supposed to have originated in Western civilization.

Civil engineers tell us that in less than fifty years, after keen young Chinamen have had access to technical schools of grade like our own, there will be no place in the engineering work of the Far East for the white expert. Rapidly energetic Chinese business men are getting into their own hands banking, coastwise navigation, trade and commerce, hitherto in the hands of foreigners. China is sitting up in bed and rubbing her eyes; when she is fully awake all signs point to her as a future bearer of civilization. "But," as a clever missionary has said, "it is easier to wake up than to get up."

"The best stuff in Asia."   In spite of the Chinese wall of inherited conservatism, in spite of the conditions of human life which have given rise to the saying, "You can smell China as you approach it a hundred miles out to sea," there is promise of the dawn of a new day for China which we do not find in India. Isabella Bird Bishop declared, "After eight and a half years of journeyings among Asiatic peoples, I say unhesitatingly that the raw material out of which the Holy Ghost fashions the Chinese convert and oftentimes the Chinese martyr is the best stuff in Asia."

2. Religion and Life

We who enjoy the privileges of enlightened Western civilization know that it owes its commanding superiority to the commanding superiority of the religion which has imparted to it its noblest characteristics. While these characteristics are not in full control we may yet say it is Christian civilization.

Chinese civilization, as it has been in the past, is not less the product, in great measure, of its religion. What, then, is the religion of China? Briefly, there are here found three fountain heads of so-called religion and from no one of them issues a stream of living water. First, we have the teachings of Confucius,—a philosopher of the sixth century B.C.,—moral but sterile. Second, we have a corrupt and idolatrous form of Buddhism, a religion which at best knew no God and no hope for the future life beyond the transmigration of souls and ultimate annihilation. Third is Taoism which holds up for worship a host of gods, genii, heroes, demons, natural forces, a grotesque medley of crude and tawdry superstitions. Du Bose says, "There is little hope for China politically, morally or religiously until Taoism is swept from the face of the land. It is evil and only evil."

But underlying these three cults, sustaining and transcending them, is the worship of ancestors, "the Gibraltar of Chinese belief." This is the major operating influence in the common round of life.

Religions of Fear. The prevailing motive of religion in China, in whatever form, is fear, not love. Fear in religion inevitably creates superstition. A religion of fear is closely connected with cruelty in the treatment of human suffering. Hence the religion of China brings us swiftly to the current conceptions of human disease, its causes and its cure.

Man is "incurably religious," and he becomes like that which he worships. China's religion has saturated her people with fear. Where there is fear, there is no hope, there is no faith, there can be no love. Such thoughts are not in all their imaginations! What can be more unreasonable than one who is possessed by fear, whether it be an animal or a man? A frightened child cannot be reasoned with; he can but tremble despite all reason. Every doctor is familiar with the hopelessness of the patient who is full of fear; he knows that the fear is almost worse than the disease. The untaught adults of China have child minds, poisoned by fear. The source of this fear is a corrupt priesthood whose business is to promote fear. Without fear their coffers would be empty, without ignorance their power would cease. When sickness comes, with no knowledge of a God of Love, or of His abundant Life, this normal condition becomes exaggerated.

Dread of demons. Fear becomes like a terrible contagion; the demons are angry, they must be propitiated lest a worse thing befall; the priest directs the curative measures, extending his jurisdiction even beyond the grave. Men do not reason when they are driven by fear and China is obsessed by it. The people firmly believe in the existence of demons of whom they are terribly afraid. To their minds hideous devils infest dark corners and lie in wait to injure passers-by often for no cause whatever.

"This dread of the spirits," says Dr. Dennis in *Christian Missions and Social Progress*, "overshadows the whole life of the Chinese. It gives to Geomancy its paralyzing influence, since it is dangerous to disturb the natural configuration of the earth, lest it excite the fatal animosity of spirits of evil. Grading for a railway becomes presumptuous trifling with unseen foes; mining for coal, iron, copper, silver and other metals is simply a blasphemous assault upon strongholds of demons. At every turn the Chinese has to reckon with impending calamity."* In *Chinese Characteristics*, page 104, the author expresses the conviction that the true root of the Chinese practice of filial piety is a mixture of fear and self-love, two of the most powerful motives which can act on the human soul. The spirits must be worshipped on account of the power which they have for evil. Dr. Henry says, "The people are chained to the dead. They cannot move or act without encountering prosperous or adverse influences excited by spirits of the dead. They are kept all their lifetime in fear, not of death, but of the dead."

Now let us see what these ancient religions of fear have, in the process of time, produced for the physical life of the race.

Bird's-eye view.   Dr. Martin Edwards on his return from a visit to China in the interest of a scheme for establishing a Harvard Medical School at some center in that land issued a report in which he sought to make clear the medical needs of China. He said: "Imagine if you will our country of ninety millions of people, with its splendid institutions for the preserving and betterment of public health.

---

* Geomancy is the belief held by the Chinese in relation to the spirits or genii that rule over winds and waters, especially running streams and subterranean waters. This doctrine is universal and inveterate among the Chinese, and, in great measure, prompts their hostility to railroads and telegraphs, since they believe that such structures anger the spirits of the air and waters and, consequently, cause floods and typhoons.

The Uplift of China, p. 13.

Now, in order to get a real conception of what China is, we are going to begin a process of elimination. First, we will take out of this country of ours all the hospitals save one hundred and sixty, that being the number there are in all China. Next, take away every infants' hospital and every hospital that is given to taking care of the mother in her hour of need. Next, we must close the greater number of the dispensaries for our poorer people and leave them without care. Let us go further and dismiss from every city the Boards of Health. The sewers, then, of each city must be filled up and all the various institutions that are acting to preserve good, healthful conditions for the individual and the city must close their doors. Now, it seems as though that is enough to take away from this country of ours, but we will have to do more yet. All our medical schools save one, and that established three years ago, must disappear. We will go still further and take away from our ninety millions of people all the scientific knowledge of how disease is caused and how it is transmitted. Then, take this forlorn country and pack it full of tuberculosis, put it in every home. Leave no city without smallpox. Scatter everywhere the other countless diseases which we have here in greater or less extent. Then place on the southeastern area bubonic plague. See that no state of the Atlantic Coast is free from the devastation of cholera. Then all over this stricken country spread the loathsome leprosy, and when all that is done, summon just four times as many people, all of whom desire as much as we to be healthy and strong, and whose hearts, strangely enough, love and suffer and break even as ours, and then say: Here's where you must live,—and that is China."

As we view the appalling extent of human suffering indicated by Dr. Edwards's sketch,* the question of Chinese remedial measures, the native practices of medicine and surgery, naturally confronts us. Here we pause, unwilling to enter far into a chamber of horrors which can only inspire us with repulsion and turn sympathy into despair. Moreover, the use of violence and torture to drive out supposed demons, of witches' brew, of snakes' skin, coffin nails and the like, of opium ever and always, belongs to a phase of development in China doomed to pass away in the light of the better day now dawning. We will pass over, then, details of native practice at this point. When we look into the medical work of Christian missionaries we shall be sufficiently convinced that ignorance and superstition, in China as in India, have done their worst, and that the woes of the women and children cry aloud piercingly for relief.

3. The Women of China

Inferiority. In the Chinese scheme of things the universe is divided between *Yang*, good, and *Yin*, evil or darkness. Demons are *Yin*; woman is *Yin*.† In the curious and complex hieroglyphics which in the Chinese system take the place of our alphabet, three women together stand for

---

* This report of Dr. Edwards was published in *The Work of the Medical Missionary*, S. V. M., 1909. Since then the number of hospitals and schools of medicine has been increased.

† See *The Changing Chinese*, Edward A. Ross, p. 187.

"intrigue." Distinctly, woman is an inferior being, a necessary evil, to be diligently kept in her place. One of the sacred sayings of Confucius runs as follows: "Women are as different from men as earth is from heaven. Women, indeed, are human beings, but they are of a lower state than men and can never attain to full equality with them. The aim of female education, therefore, is perfect submission, not cultivation and development of the mind."

A logical development of twenty-six centuries of Confucianism is a civilization in which only one woman in a thousand can read.

Subjection. A very ancient book exists in China called "Rules for Women." It consists of seven chapters. The subjects of these chapters, as given below, fairly illustrate the place of women in China's social scheme.

1. The state of subjection and weakness in which women are born.

2. The duties of a woman when under the power of a husband.

3. The unlimited respect due to a husband, and constant self-examination and restraint.

4. The qualities which render a female lovable, divided into those relating to her virtue, her conversation, her dress and occupations.

5. The lasting attachment due from a wife to a husband.

6. The obedience due to a husband and to his parents.

7. The cordial relations to be maintained with her husband's brothers and sisters.

Seclusion.   It is wholly logical in these views of the subordination of women that seclusion goes with them. Why should any one care to converse with a woman? At best she cannot be trusted. A student of things Chinese writes of being entertained for three days in the home of a wealthy silk merchant in an inland city and during that time never once catching a glimpse of any of the ladies of the household. There must have been a number of them, for the Chinaman of means is both polygamous and patriarchal. Several wives are in order, and when the sons marry they bring their wives home to the paternal roof. Idle and vacant to a degree is life in the women's apartments, into which only a woman can gain access. It is a life wholly destitute of large, impersonal interests; its effects are mental and moral emptiness.

Foot-binding.   The fashion of small feet is supposed to have passed away by the edict of the late Empress Dowager. But age-long customs are not changed immediately, even by edict. People are so much accustomed to this practice that most men would refuse to wed a woman whose feet are of the natural size. Mothers who are careless in every point relative to their daughters bestow extreme diligence in bandaging and guarding against every attempt which the child may make to relieve herself from the painful pressure. Somehow the vast importance of the condition is impressed upon the child and, when this occurs, the martydom necessary for attaining it is cheerfully endured.

A Chinese saying tells us that "for every pair of bound feet there has been a whole tubful of tears" and they add that one girl out of ten dies of foot-binding or its after effects.

In searching for the origin of the custom, it is found that the Chinese themselves are not certain what gave rise to it. "Who would have thought it possible fifteen years ago that not only would the Manchu Empress Dowager have issued an edict upon the subject, but even Chinese Viceroys would take up the matter with enthusiasm? Credit is largely due to Mrs. Archibald Little for having patiently, persistently, intelligently and intelligibly placed the advantages and disadvantages, mundane and spiritual, in a sympathetic way before the literary classes; and, lo and behold, popular prejudice collapses at once. Probably foot-binding will go on fitfully and locally for another hundred years, but its back is broken."

It is within bounds to say that even in this late day of progress there are seventy million women tottering about in China on deformed and tortured feet.

Opium. Few realize the extent of the use of opium and its hold upon all ages. Dr. McCartney of Chung King says that women are addicted to smoking opium, not so much as men, but from what can be learned from patients in the dispensary, about fifteen to twenty per cent. of the women smoke,—all ages from infancy to ninety years. The parents blow smoke into the face of the infant in arms in order to soothe it to sleep. They seem to be bound, as it were, with chains by the habit, and even though they realize its terrible ravages they are helpless to help themselves.

Infanticide. In view of the low estimate of women, and the slight regard for the sacredness of human life, we are prepared for two piteous facts in Chinese domestic life, female infanticide and suicide. " 'Are baby girls still killed at birth?' is often asked us," writes Dr. Mabel Hannington. " 'Many of them are,' reply those of us who know."

"Every now and then one reads a paper by someone, who thinks he knows, in which the statement is made that the practice of infanticide has been greatly exaggerated. Much of it, it is true, does not appear on the surface; an epidemic disease, such as plague, may occasionally make a shortage of girls, but it is still frightfully common. The writer has arrived at a house to find the first of a pair of twins, a girl, dead on the ground, deliberately murdered, and has, after a long struggle, saved the lives of a mother and her little girl, to find on the visit next day, that the latter had been put out of the way. One knows of women who have killed four, five, and even six children."   (*Medical Missions*, 1914.)

Dr. Mabel Poulter reports that quite fifty per cent. and perhaps even seventy per cent. of the death rate amongst children is due to tetanus, a disease which is caused by uncleanly methods in connection with childbirth. This is, however, only one of the many diseases which affect infant mortality. The cruelty to female children sold as slaves is appalling.

The girl in China, as in India, is never welcome. From her infancy she is a burden, because she cannot perpetuate ancestral worship, nor be a permanent member of her own family. She makes an extra mouth to feed and there are no "scruples" to prevent her being strangled, drowned in a cesspool, or thrown away. There seems not to be the custom of child widowhood, but betrothal takes place early enough to rob her of her girlhood. "It is the custom" is the answer to which there is no reply if inquiry is made as to why. Betrothal is less expensive when girls are young, the cost being from fifty cents to two dollars, while it may cost ten dollars or more when the girl is older, and business is business when it comes even to matrimony. It may be that a debt may need to be cancelled or the husband's family is in need of a maid of all work and the daughter-in-law is less likely to leave and costs less than a servant. The undivided family plan adds to her misery, she encounters strife perpetual, with the advantage on the side of her mother-in-law. She may have a necklace of bruises from pinchings around her neck, a favorite home treatment, or her body beaten; and when in time she becomes a wife it is not customary to introduce her, even among the well-to-do. She may, if mentioned at all, be referred to as the 'unworthy inner one' or 'the inside of the house.' In any case, she is the property of her husband, to be put away at his will.

Suicide. The subjection, the seclusion, not so rigid as in India, but oppressive, the cruelties and exactions of life, above all its emptiness, are sufficient explanation for the frequency of suicide among Chinese women and girls, five or ten times greater than among males. The perpetual repression of natural feelings, ambitions, and desires, is bound to have a disastrous reaction upon young wives and widows. Suicide by use of opium among them or by throwing themselves into canals and wells bears abundant testimony to the desperation which seethes below the calm surface of domestic life.

Maternity. Native Chinese treatments of prospective mothers and conditions consequent upon motherhood without intelligent care, are untellable. Women physicians see them until the whole head is sick and the heart faint. The following experience is reported by Dr. Bixby of Kityang: "In obstetrics more than in any other branch of the work, we are called upon to witness the pitiful ignorance and superstition of the people. In one case we arrived just in time to rescue a young woman who was being hung, because she had a slight hemorrhage and had fainted, and was supposed to be in labor, though she was not. A ladder had been brought in and stood upright and to this she was tied by her hair and supported by a high stool only and there she was being pounded and pinched to drive out the evil spirits. When we arrived she had been unconscious for some time and was almost pulseless. With some difficulty we got her down, laid her in bed, applied restoratives and she recovered, and a month later gave birth to a baby boy."

Dr. Rachel Benn describes most graphically how "it need not have been." Incidentally, also, she answers the oft-repeated assertion that such things happen only among the slum people.

"It was in the middle of a hot June afternoon in Tientsin, when, with many a flourish on the part of the chair-bearers, a sedan chair was set down at the doctor's door.

Medical Missionary pulling a tooth, India

Witch Doctor and the Kraal for her Goats
Inhambane, Africa

"The fine covering, the blue silk lining, the screens on the windows, the fluttering sunshade of soft black silk at the top of the windows, and, most of all, the flaming tassels of long red wool which adorned the hats of the bearers, proclaimed the chair to be that of a mandarin. The swelling pride with which the gatekeeper ushered into the doctor's study an Important Individual who carried in his hand a leather cardcase a foot long and six inches wide, further proclaimed that momentous fact. Opening the cardcase and extracting a large red calling card used by the Chinese, the Important Individual presented it, saying, 'The fourth wife of Yen-Great-Man has difficulty in childbearing and the Great-Man begs the doctor to come.' "

"Taking the obstetrical bag that she kept always ready, the doctor was soon being rapidly carried toward the yamen—the Important Individual running ahead calling out 'Scrape your shins!' 'Open your head,' or in plain English, 'Clear the way.' "

"Arriving at the yamen, the doctor found incense smoking in a bronze burner before the main entrance in the women's court, and E-tai-tai, or first wife, waiting to receive her. The servant who helped the doctor from the chair and led her to the lady did so with an air of mystery and fear. The lady received her in the same awe-struck manner, and taking her hand led her into the reception room, saying in a low voice, 'Doctor, sin lurks in our home. Our babies are all girls. We have made a pilgrimage to the temple to the goddess of maternity, given alms, burned incense not a little, and prayed Kuan-Yin to send us a boy this time, and now because of some unknown sin of this woman she is going to die before the child is born. If you have skill, please, please, help us.'

"A servant entered and said, 'The Great-Man would speak with the doctor.' He repeated the first wife's name, adding, 'I have had the best of mid-wives. I have taken no account of spending money. I have even sent and got the sacred-pill-of-the-sea at seventy-five dollars apiece. Fourth wife has swallowed two of them and even they have done no good. If you can help us to obtain a son, we will reward you and give you a great name.'

"The doctor wishing to see the sacred-pill-of-the-sea the Great-Man took from his purse a disk of sea-shell about two-thirds the size of a cent, bearing upon its face the mystical symbol of the dual powers of nature. The patient had swallowed two of them.

" 'I have learned many good ways of helping,' said the doctor, 'and if you will lead me to the patient I will do my best.'

"As she was leaving the room, the Great-Man said, 'Excuse me, Doctor, one moment, please. Can you tell the sex of a child before it is born?' Without waiting for a reply he continued eagerly, 'If you can and this one is a boy, save it even if you have to kill the mother. If it is a girl, kill it. We have more female slaves now than we want.'

"The poor mother! Not a throb of compassion. She was only the unworthy medium by which a son might be obtained.

"With a heavy heart the doctor followed E-tai-tai from the room, past the family shrine where incense

burning made the air heavy with its sickening odor,
to the door of her patient's room. The door was
opened just wide enough to admit the ladies and
instantly closed behind them. 'Please open a window
or a door,' the doctor pleaded. 'It will not do,' rose
the voices of the half-dozen women in the room.

"A luxurious bed stood in one corner of the room,
high posted and hung around with silk curtains
closely drawn, completely shutting in the occupant.
Cautiously opening the curtains a little way the
attendants thrust the doctor inside and swiftly
closed them again. Stifling with the heat and lack
of air, and in an agony of soul for fear she was
going to die with an unborn child and so be doomed
to an eternity of torment—an agony of soul which
was worse than her agony of body, great as it was—
sat a young girl. Folding her trembling hands, she
raised them in supplication and fixed her beseeching
eyes upon the doctor with a mute prayer for help
that would have melted a heart of stone. Mystical
characters written on red paper were pasted on her
temples, an amulet hung round her neck and an old
midwife sat on the bed behind her, holding her up
and rhythmically slapping the back of her head,
keeping time to a dismal chant.

" 'I must have air, I cannot breathe in here,'
remonstrated the doctor as she tried to open the
curtains. But resolute hands held them close and
a voice outside said, 'We dare not.'

" 'Why? What do you fear?'

" 'The doctor is an outside-country person and
doesn't understand,' the voice replied, 'Every house

where birth is taking place is surrounded by dis-
embodied spirits, eagerly watching for a chance to
enter and take possession of the mother's body.
They come in as fresh air and we must keep them
out.'

" 'Stop chanting, and stop slapping the Tao-tai's
head and lay her down,' the doctor commanded the
midwife.

" 'Not so,' she retorted. 'It keeps the evil influences away and if she lies down the child will come
up through the mouth.'

" 'Great Lady,' called the doctor to the first
wife outside, 'why have they covered this woman
with a man's garment and put men's shoes on the
foot of the bed?'

" 'Oh! that is to give her strength to bear the
child.'

"In the end the doctor was able to convince them
that she could save the mother and child if they
would eliminate the midwife, ventilate the room
and let her have her way. Near midnight the doctor
went home, overwhelmed with gratitude, praise and
presents, leaving a rejoicing family, for the baby
proved to be a boy after all, although they all declared it must be a good-for-nothing girl, for no boy
would be so unfilial as to cause his mother such
suffering.

"Five days later, the doctor was again hurried
to the yamen, this time on the run, wherever the
bearers could run.

"A stricken family stood round the divan on
which the precious boy lay. Down they went before
the doctor, knocking their heads and imploring her

to save life. Reaching to lift the little one, a servant caught the doctor's arm and whispered, 'Don't touch it, it has a devil.' Assuring them that she, being a follower of Jesus Christ, had no fear of devils, the doctor took the little thing that none of them dared touch and laid it in her lap. It was dying. Noticing blood on the baby's lips, she opened the mouth and found that the artery under the tongue had been punctured several times by the needle of a Chinese doctor. A great wave of compassion for those poor people who, in their blind superstition, had done the cruel thing, swept into the doctor's heart, and with swimming eyes and faltering voice, she cried out, 'Oh! why did you do this. You have killed your baby!' 'No, no,' cried the heart-broken father. 'Those are very cruel words you have spoken. Would we harm a son whom we wanted more than anything else on earth? A devil was in it twisting its body in convulsions, and there was no way to dislodge it except by sticking with needles under the tongue. Oh, no,' he continued vehemently, 'we didn't kill our son. It never was a child. It was a demon sent in the form of a son to cause great suffering at its birth and then die and wring our hearts with the greatest of disappointments. It is all on account of the wickedness of the women of our household. I am a marked man!' and he went from the room in despair, as the doctor rose and gently laid the little dead baby upon the couch."

The woman herself. We have been pondering a dozen or more serious, and very serious, handicaps under which the Chinese woman labors, but they all seem to fade into a misty vagueness when she herself appears. Have you seen her, the Christian Chinese girl, in this country? If so, you have been astonished. For, instead of the timid, cringing nonentity which you expected, driven by demon-fears and social cruelties to something less than a cipher, you have met a graceful, bright-eyed, bright-witted young woman, with a distinct and delicate sense of humor, an equally distinct, albeit gentle self-confidence, combined with deference to elders peculiarly pleasing here among us. Our Chinese girl student moves among her fellow-students in our American colleges as one to the manner born, not at all overawed but even less self-assertive or complacent.

Li. While it must be emphasized that those who come among us have been long under Christian influences in China, perhaps the quality which impresses us most in them is peculiar to their nation and their native training; this is their intuitive perception of that which is fitting, something more than good taste, deeper than decorum. The effort to define it sends us back to the mysterious and significant Chinese word, *Li*. Originally indicative of religious devotion and ceremonial and the ritual of sacrifice, this term has come to embrace the complete round of social life, including manners and conduct. Reverence for personality, filial piety, sincerity, correct speech are included in it, but more than this, to use the words of a thoughtful writer,* "*Li* controls the thoughts

* See "The Christian Opportunity in Regard to the Women of China," by Luella Miner, *International Review of Missions*, April, 1917.

of the heart no less surely than the acts of the body." Here we find the secret of the dignity and poise which undeniably belong to the Chinese woman at home or abroad, in contradistinction from the passive pathos of the Indian woman. This characteristic may be rooted also in the sure knowledge of the Chinese woman that, when the wife becomes the mother of a boy, she is bound to emerge from her status of subjection to one of something like authority. Filial piety is owed as much to the mother as to the father in China.

Brain power. In intellectual capacity there are no "brainier" women anywhere than the Chinese, on the testimony of competent observers. An official statement of the Young Women's Christian Association of China in 1910 contains the following expression: "Let none think Chinese women inferior to those of any other land. There is no line of study or of effort in which they do not excel and no height of character to which they do not attain."

The mental initiative of the young Chinese women in this country is well illustrated by the following experience:

Several Chinese college girls, Indemnity Students, were spending their first Christmas holidays in America in a home in New England.

Their hostess, anxious to entertain them according to their desires, said, "I have left three days for you to plan for. There must be places you would like to visit in Boston or things you would especially enjoy doing. Please tell me, as I would like to plan for your pleasure."

Six eager faces looked into hers. The first girl

said, "I would like so much to go to the Imbecile School"; another broke in, "And I to the Perkins Institute for the Blind." "But," said the bewildered hostess, who had not thought of this sort of Christmas holiday diversion, "I do not understand what pleasure you could possibly get from visiting an imbecile school." "You know," was the quick answer, "that there is one of the finest schools for the feeble-minded in the world near Boston. I want to learn how they teach, so that I can help such children in China." Thus each one expressed her mind and all the wishes were gratified, including an X-ray demonstration.

There is a great new hope for China in the enlightened devotion of the Chinese students who come among us. These girls, with few exceptions, are Christians and were trained in our mission schools.

Can any one doubt the ability of educated Chinese women to render effective service to their suffering sisters as Christian physicians?

Medical schools. There are already in China three medical schools for women. The Peking Medical School for Women, teaching in Mandarin; the Soo Chow Women's Medical School, teaching in English; and the Hackett Medical College for Women of Canton, teaching in Cantonese. Geographically they are far removed from one another and no two are teaching in the same language. The Peking School has fifty-eight students in three classes; the Soo Chow school, thirteen students in two classes; and the Canton, twenty-five students in four classes. In June, 1916, five girls

graduated from the Soo Chow Medical College after
the completion of a five year's medical course in
English. Already twelve hospitals have applied for
these girls as assistant physicians. Consideration of
the work, present and prospective, of these schools
is reserved for our last chapter.

4. How Christianity Brings Healing

Three months after the death of the pioneer
Christian missionary to China, Robert Morrison
(term of service 1807-1834), there arrived in the
port of Canton the first medical missionary to
China, Dr. Peter Parker. His remarkable skill in
surgery overcame the iron prejudices of the Chinese
against the stranger; his cures were pronounced
miraculous and his fame spread throughout the
eighteen provinces. In 1835 Dr. Parker opened the
first medical missionary hospital in China, medical
work thus receiving permanent shape.

First aid.   It was about forty years between the
advent of Dr. Parker in Canton and
that of the first woman medical missionary for
China, Dr. Lucinda Coombs, sent by the Woman's Foreign Missionary Society of the Methodist
Episcopal Church, as was Dr. Clara Swain, and, like
Dr. Swain, a graduate of the Woman's Medical
College of Pennsylvania. In 1875 Dr. Coombs opened
the first hospital for women in China. In 1879 Dr.
Caroline Daniels was sent to Swatow by the American Baptist Woman's Foreign Missionary Society
of the West. Dr. Mary Holbrook, a graduate of the
Medical Department of Michigan University, was

the first appointee of the Congregational Women's Board, her station Tung-cho. The Woman's Board of the Interior, in 1881, sent Dr. Murdock to Kalgan, on the borders of Mongolia. In 1882 Dr. Mary F. Niles was sent to Canton by the Woman's Foreign Missionary Society of the Presbyterian Church. The list of pioneer medical women missionaries to China, included in the years between 1873 and 1883, closes with an illustrious name, that of Dr. Elizabeth Reifsnyder, sent in 1883 to Shanghai by the Woman's Union Missionary Society.

There are today four hundred and fifty-three missionary physicians on the field in China, three hundred and forty-five men, one hundred and eight women, and two hundred and forty-four hospitals. But China's population is four hundred million and one large American city would show more than four hundred qualified physicians. From a report on medical work in China published by the Woman's Foreign Missionary Society of the Presbyterian Church we give the following summary:

Summary of work.   What are these agencies, small and scattered as they are, doing for China?

1. They are giving the services of a band of qualified men and women, who are devoting their lives to healing service, asking no other reward.

2. They are establishing a chain of hospitals and dispensaries throughout the land to serve as centres of sanitary science and benevolent help.

3. They are maintaining a small group of asylums for special classes—the insane, the blind, the deaf, the lepers—to serve as models for future advance.

4. They are furnishing a small army of native physicians and nurses, trained in the old days by the pioneers with self-denying

patience, now instructed in good schools sustained by joint efforts.

5. They are translating the best medical books, without which the schools would be hopelessly hampered, and carrying on research work in special lines.

6. They are helping to rid the country of the awful opium curse. All our hospitals treat hundreds of opium cases yearly.

7. The direct results of the medical work in bringing souls to Christ are not small.

The medical missionaries are always in the forefront of the battle against plague and cholera, and conspicuous in every movement for better living. All this is done at very small expense. A single hospital in one of our large American cities costs yearly far more than all our work in China put together.

Hospital routine. Dr. Emily Bretthauer, head of the Baptist Woman's Hospital at Hanyang, Central China, describes in few and comprehensive words the leading characteristics of her work, which we give as representative. Evangelization and doctoring go hand in hand in all departments. The work is divided into three departments: out-patient, in-patient, and nurses' training school. The out-patient department includes the work in the dispensary, in the office, and professional visits to the homes of the natives. In the dispensary many women receive their introduction to Christianity. A Chinese woman rarely comes alone; a relative or two, or even three, must come along to see what is going on, and so it does not take long before there is a whole room full of women who are listening to the Gospel message. Some of them come a long time before dispensary hours, even as much as four hours before. During the time of waiting the Bible woman speaks personally to each patient as she comes in, and when they are all gathered together she preaches to them until the arrival of the doctor. The doctor with the native nurses then sees to the physical wants of the patients. She sees each patient herself and speaks words of consolation or cheer as well as prescribes medicine. A large number of the patients in the dispensary are of the poorer classes, some even of the beggars from the street.

As the more well-to-do Chinese women do not care to mix with the poorer classes, we have arranged for them to come to the *doctor's office*, paying, of course, a larger fee. These patients are received by a tactful native nurse, and over the inevitable cup of tea their minds are led from the usual polite talk to that which is nearest and dearest to our hearts. While they tell us of their ills, we tell them of Him who is able to save the soul as well as to heal the body.

As to the *calls at the homes*, these include all classes, from those of the very poorest to those of the highest officials. Here is an unusual opportunity for telling of Jesus. As soon as the doctor and native nurses enter the house, if it is of a poor woman, say a hut, all the women of the neighboring huts come crowding in, so there is soon an audience as large as one cares to have. These people are good listeners, too.

In the hospital women and children are brought under the influence of the Gospel for a much longer period, some even for months. It is our special opportunity for the children.

The popular prejudice against and fear of foreigners at first holds both children and women at a distance, but these dissolve on acquaintance. An instance may be given of a woman severely ill who needed hospital treatment. She hesitated long, "because," she said, "I have been told that the foreign people cut out the hearts and the eyes of the Chinese, so it is not safe to have anything to do with them." However, she decided to come into the hospital and have her operation. After she went back home she did much to overcome prejudice in her village. "I am an example of the love which these Christian people have for the Chinese," she was wont to say. As in India, the women marvel at the cleanliness, the tender treatment, the peaceful atmosphere which they find in the hospital; above all, at the willingness of the foreign medical ladies to perform for them menial service which their own mothers would not do.

What is true in this hospital is essentially descriptive of the work in all mission hospitals for women in China. Since women are prevented by custom from seeking help from male physicians, the need of an adequate number of native women practitioners is apparent. It would seem that if there is a place in all the world where a woman's trained touch is indispensable it is in Chinese mission hospitals for women. There can be no question of ability, when such work is being done as was described by Dr. Irving Ludlow of Cleveland, Ohio, in his observations on medical progress in the Orient. He was, when in China, asked to operate on three or four very serious cases (all major operations in which women here have but rarely been allowed to do more than look on at a safe and worshipful distance), with the Chinese women as assistant surgeons. The proposal at first seemed to him preposterous. "Could it be possible that Chinese women could be so far advanced as to carry out the technique of abdominal surgery?" But again the old proverb, "Seeing is believing" was fulfilled, and he reports "that a more neat, dignified, calm, and skilful staff would be hard to find. Not only are they good as assistants, but some of the graduates perform operations with excellent results. One in particular is an exceedingly clever and careful surgeon, and only a few weeks previous to my visit had removed successfully an ovarian cyst, weighing eighty pounds. This same surgeon has had an enormous obstetrical experience, most of the cases being out of the ordinary, for it is rarely that a physician would be summoned for a normal case." He writes, furthermore: "It has been almost imperative that work for women be kept entirely separate, for it is only within the last few years that men have been allowed to have any part in the care of women. Many, particularly of the higher class, would doubtless prefer death rather than allow a man to take charge of them."

5. Three Life-saving Stations

The forty-six years of Christian women's medical work for women of China has resulted in a series of hospitals, extending,—at sadly wide removes one from another, indeed,—over the vast territory. Each one is a beacon light sending out its rays of compassion over the sea of suffering humanity. Whether larger or smaller, each one of these hospitals is a life-saving station; all are dedicated to the Great

Physician in whose name they exist and whose command they follow. In order to come into touch with all, we choose three for illustration, three which nobly represent the series: namely, the Margaret Williamson Hospital at Shanghai, the David Gregg Hospital at Canton, and the Danforth Memorial Hospital at Kiu Kiang. These are chosen, in particular, as being widely separated geographically, and each as holding a point of strategic importance. Take a map of China, and, having cut from paper an obtuse-angled triangle, lay it along the coast, the obtuse angle to the right, the lower acute angle touching Canton on the south, the upper angle resting on Shanghai far to the north. Look inland, then, to the valley of the Yangtse River and you will find that the obtuse angle,—if you have the requisite proportions,—precisely touches the city of Kiu Kiang. So your triangle brings before you two great and widely separated seaports of China and a typical inland, provincial city.

Three famous women. The Christian hospitals in these three cities owe much to the potent personality of three physicians presiding over them: Dr. Elizabeth Reifsnyder, Dr. Mary Fulton, and Dr. Mary Stone. Let us find our way first to the city of Shanghai, since its hospital was first founded.

Station number 1, Shanghai. It is now not far from forty years since Mrs. Margaret Williamson appeared at the Board Rooms of the Woman's Union Missionary Society in New York with the first money towards the erection of the hospital that bears her name, because it was built by her generosity. Mrs. Williamson was one of the early mem-

bers of this Board, the *first* Woman's Board of
Foreign Missions, which celebrated its fiftieth anniversary in January, 1911. As a consequence of this
initial action of Mrs. Williamson, Dr. Elizabeth
Reifsnyder arrived in Shanghai September first,
1883, and there began the study of the Chinese
language and the practice of medicine.

In April, 1884, having been joined by Miss Mc-
Kechnie (now Mrs. E. H. Thomson), a trained nurse,
Dr. Reifsnyder hired two rooms and opened a
dispensary in the native city, inside the West Gate.
Here patients were seen three afternoons in the
week, and here the work went on steadily until
June, 1885, when the hospital was opened. The road
leading to this dispensary was not a pleasant one;
only the grace of God could help one to travel it
day after day, for there was so much that was most
offensive to one's several senses. During this year
of dispensary work in those quarters with their mud
floors and bare benches, despite ups and downs,
almost four thousand patients were treated.

The first piece of land for the Margaret Williamson Hospital was secured in 1883, the year of the
donor's death. Her name lives and will live in years
to come in the hearts of thousands, and she will ever
be remembered as one of China's great benefactors.
To this first piece of land eight more have been
added, all lying well out of the city limits. Upon
this ground were erected the main building, the
home for medical workers, the maternity hospital
and the house for nurses and assistants, all gifts of
friends at home supplemented by notable generosity
on the part of Chinese citizens.

DR. ESTHER KIM PAK, KOREA

Over and beyond the regular work of the hospital is its function of serving as a home of refuge from the ills and trials of life. Many homeless and afflicted waifs have found here a home and a chance, in the end, to render loving service. The evangelistic side of the work is of great importance. It has been truly said, "Life is but a means unto an end, and that end God," and this purpose hospital life seeks to serve. The evangelistic work is in charge of Misses Mary and Elizabeth Irvine, who not only spend much time in the wards, but who follow up a great many patients in their homes, making long trips into the country by boat and wheelbarrow. Hundreds of towns and villages are represented at the dispensary and in the wards by women and children in the course of years, sometimes a hundred in a single year. It may be seen that a physician in charge of a hospital in China, with an annual clientele of some fifty thousand daily patients and some eight hundred in-patients and the entire charge of administration, must have mind and hands fully occupied. The success of the administration is shown by the fact that the larger part of the support for the Margaret Williamson Hospital is met by receipts from Chinese patients. On the occasion of its twenty-fifth anniversary, June 4, 1911, Dr. Reifsnyder was able to report eight hundred thousand patients treated in the Hospital since its foundation. Much more might be said, but the work will speak for itself in the years to come, and "to God be the glory."

Station number 2, Canton. The Rev. Albert A. Fulton went to China as a missionary (American

Presbyterian) in 1880. Four years later he was joined in Canton by his sister, Mary Fulton, a qualified physician. She will speak to us through her letters in which we listen to the voice of a courageous, ardent, consecrated soldier in the Battalion of Life. As Dr. Fulton will by no means sound her own trumpet and as the sentences from her letters are, of necessity, fragments, let us introduce her by saying that, when she reached China, she chose to carry on her work in a notoriously hostile province, until she was driven back to Canton with a price upon her head. Through her steadfast waiting and tireless labors in Canton there has developed from the humblest beginnings the threefold work, Hospital, Medical College, and Nurses' Training School, of which she will presently make mention.

The property consists of one and one-half acres of land, with seven buildings, in the western suburb of Canton. The buildings are of grey brick, and open on all sides to the light and air. The older buildings accommodate the chapel, dining rooms, laboratories, and recitation rooms. The main hospital, rebuilt in 1913, is provided with every modern facility for ventilation and cleanliness. There is a specially well-equipped operating department, built according to the requirements of modern surgery and clinical instruction.

Enter Dr. Fulton. Hongkong, China, October 11, 1884. After years of preparation and a journey of seven thousand miles, I am at last in this great Empire of China.

* * * * *

August, 1895. In the last two years I have accomplished very little that can be tabulated. We rented two shops, one for a chapel, the other for dispensing. Every day at noon the chapel doors are thrown open for preaching. The dispensary is open daily. Some women who, when they came for treatment, had never heard of God's existence, are now members of church. When we began services at this place, scarcely half a dozen attended; yesterday there were nearly a hundred. What we need and what I am daily praying for is a women's and children's hospital, with a room large enough to accommodate all who would come to church. It seems like hoping against hope, but power is with God, who can turn the hearts of men toward this much-needed place for healing and worship. I shall keep on knocking until some one hears. This small shop is the only place for Christian worship in all this part of a great heathen city, wholly given to idolatry.

March, 1901. My brother writes from America that money has been given by Lafayette Avenue Church, Brooklyn, for a woman's hospital. Fifteen years I have longed, worked, prayed for this.

August. Mr. E. A. J. Hackett, of Fort Wayne, Indiana, has given money to build a medical college for women. I couldn't find words in the English language to express my delight and gratitude.

October, 1901. A Chinese gentleman came in with over one thousand dollars in straw bags, which his servant placed upon the table. I was amazed. Mr. L—— said that several gentlemen had been asked to contribute this sum to a benevolent object. Some trouble arose and they decided to give it to the David Gregg Hospital. This, with money contributed by Mr. John H. Converse, furnished the building with the most necessary articles.

David Gregg Hospital for Women and Children was formally opened April 23, 1902.

In connection with the hospital will be the Julia M. Turner Training School for Nurses. The course will require two years.

Hackett Medical College for Women was opened December 17, 1902.

(April 1, 1903, to October 13, 1904, Dr. Fulton was absent on furlough.)

April, 1905. Erection of the new maternity ward begun. Mr. Hackett sent more money for a lecture hall.

While I was in Philadelphia last year, Mrs. Turner said she wished to give a maternity ward in memory of Mary H. Perkins, one of the founders of the Foreign Missionary Society. Imagine! Some one *coming, giving!* So long accustomed had I been to wait years for a building after I wanted it, that really it left one breathless from sheer astonishment. From the humble, quiet manner of the offer, one would infer a favor was being asked; that five dollars was promised instead of many thousands. But then, there is only one Mrs. Turner in the world.

June. The hospital is full, and seven beds on the verandahs. It is now entirely self-supporting.

September, 1907. College reopened. Forty-two students are studying.

China is awakening so rapidly that she is not only crying from hunger, but one may say *screaming* for immediate nourishment, in the way of books and help of every kind. What we do to supply her need is small, but is better than nothing. At intervals I have translated: *Remarkable Answers to Prayer, Diseases of Children, Nursing in Abdominal Surgery*, Penrose's *Gynecology, Hopkins's Roller Bandage.*

High lights, these scattered records, in a high career.

Station number 3, in the Yangtse Valley. In the city of Kiu-Kiang, in the year 1873, a little daughter was born to the Christian Chinese pastor and his wife, Mr. and Mrs. Shih. They gave their baby the name Mei-yu, meaning Beautiful Jewel. To the amazement of all their friends and neighbors the new little daughter was as joyously welcomed in the household of the Shihs as if she had been a son. As years went on a new cause of amazement among their neighbors was furnished, for the little Mei-yu's feet were never bound. She was the first girl brought up by her own parents in all central and western

China with unbound feet. Her playmates called her shoes "salt-junks" and ridiculed her cruelly as she ran, fleet and firm, along the streets, while they hobbled on their tortured stumps, their "lily" feet, encased in tiny toy slippers. When she was eight years old Mei-yu Shih was brought by her father and mother to the mission school in Kiu-Kiang presided over by Miss Gertrude Howe. "We have brought our little girl to you," they said. "We want you to make a doctor of her. We see how much good your American doctors are doing our people, but we feel that a Chinese woman doctor might do many things which a foreigner could not do." With gladness Miss Howe accepted the charge.

With Mei-yu there was educated a child of her own age, who had been adopted by Miss Howe when she was a new-born baby, for, being a fifth daughter, her parents had decided to sell or give her away. Miss Howe took her to her heart and named her Ida Kahn. Like Mei-yu her feet remained unbound. The free limbs of these two little girls, developed in normal fashion and their minds, not tortured by superstitious fears, grew unfettered among the crippled and stunted children around them. In 1892, Mei-yu Shih, Mary Stone, as she is now called by English-speaking people, and Ida Kahn were brought by Miss Howe to the United States to study medicine at Michigan University. Here they were graduated in 1896, and on their return to Kiu-Kiang, as Dr. Stone and Dr. Kahn, they received a wonderful ovation and at once began the practice of medicine among the women of their own people under the auspices of the Woman's Foreign

Missionary Society of the Methodist Episcopal Church.

Dr. Stone worked for several years in a little hospital only 21x28 feet in size, containing only twenty beds. However, in 1900, a well-known physician in Chicago, the late Dr. I. N. Danforth, who was strongly interested in foreign missionary work in China, especially in its relation to the introduction of modern medicine into that country, offered to build for Dr. Stone a hospital in memory of his wife. Since that time a modern hospital has been built. Inspired by her love and sympathy for suffering Chinese women, with this splendid plant in which to work, Dr. Stone has spread the fame of the Elizabeth Skelton Danforth Memorial Hospital throughout the Yangtse Valley. She has become a very skilful surgeon as well as physician. Most remarkable are the operations which she has performed.

Several times Dr. Stone has returned to America for rest and further study at Johns Hopkins. She is a forceful speaker, being winsome, witty, and inspiring. One of the best after-dinner speeches that was ever made in this country was made by the "little doctor" at a great banquet in Los Angeles. Notwithstanding her prominence, she is simple and unassuming. Her work absorbs her very life.

Dr. Stone has adopted four Chinese lads whom she is bringing up. Two are relatives, one is the son of a widowed Bible woman, and the fourth is a famine orphan. She is in charge of a home for cripples near the hospital in Kiu-Kiang. Furthermore, Dr. Stone is a leader in reform movements in China. She is a member of the China Continuation

Committee and has recently been president of the National Woman's Christian Temperance Union of China. Her life is full to overflowing.

In the year 1916, Dr. Stone treated in her hospital over twenty-four thousand cases. Her expert nurses receive only fifty dollars a year each and out of that gladly give one-tenth to the district's missionary work.

"There is a flag that flies higher than the flags of all the nations," said Dr. Stone. "It is the Red Cross flag, and I think it will sometime be the flag of all the world. And what could be more appropriate, for it symbolizes the love of Christ, expressing itself in service among men."

From a personal letter recently received from Dr. Stone we are enabled to quote as follows:

With my head so full of ideas and my heart bent on doing more for the Lord's kingdom, I returned to Kiu-Kiang from Hankow with plans for the New Year Forward Evangelistic Campaign. It was, indeed, a case where "man proposes and God disposes." I plunged right into our medical work. The city was fighting an epidemic of pneumonia. An old missionary was struck down with it also. I was tired and overheated on the steamer and caught a very bad cold and after a week's struggle to pull my pneumonia cases up I succumbed myself and, as a result, I have been a patient myself causing so much anxiety to our mission and co-workers. I have been very grateful for the quiet time I have had on my sick bed, also for the way the Lord has cared for His work among us. The concession doctor has been most kind to me and our entire mission. He has been our mission doctor as well as surgeon in the Danforth Hospital. His letter to me since I came up to Kuling will report so fully of the Lord's work, yes, your work, too, that I am tempted to put an extract in.

Extracts from Dr. Tenney's letter:

The work at your hospital is exceedingly pleasant, and also

a very valuable experience for me. I am most pleased with the two Dr. Kwangs. Dr. Kathleen gives an excellent anaesthetic, certainly far better than the average well-trained physician at home. Dr. Alice is a very clear-headed, conscientious and hard-working girl, and I am most pleased with her work.

Your hospital is a real oasis in the desert. It is a great pleasure to me to be greeted by the smiling faces of the doctors and nurses and to receive such courteous treatment from them. Without any flattery or exaggeration, I have never seen in China such a high degree of Christian character as is exhibited on the faces of your doctors and nurses at the Danforth Hospital. Whenever I hear any sneers at missionaries, as one does occasionally in the concession, my answer is, "You would change your mind if you went to Dr. Stone's hospital."

The following statistics will help our friends to understand how faithfully our workers have carried on the work. We have again graduated three nurses out of their original class of sixteen. This year we have taken another big class of freshmen. Last year we sent out a large number of graduates to take important positions throughout the country. Instead of depleting our work it has reacted in sending us more highly educated girls to study nursing.

Increasing opportunities are given us to teach, to preach and to heal. A great gospel tent was put up in our yard last fall for the conference and, instead of pulling it down, money was given us to put it in a permanent shape. We have had mass meetings, educational meetings for the masses in the city, where magic lantern slides on the life and work of Christ were shown. Lectures on hygiene, such as "Flies kill people," "The Plague," "Tuberculosis," "Mosquitoes," have been illustrated on the screen for the people.

An official is visiting Kuling. He had been troubled with insomnia for six months. General W—— recommended me as physician. I tried to refuse, because I was under orders not to work this summer. No excuse whatever was accepted, so, like an obedient subject, I went to examine him. As was expected, the political troubles in the country were uppermost in his mind. He said, "When one is besieged on all sides, what is a person to do?"

There and then was my privilege to tell him he way upwards, the ever-present help in time of need. Suffice it to say that he is very much better without the least medicine and we pray that his friendliness to the Gospel may mean eventually his own salvation and that of his household. When he returned the call the next day he said he was going to send his wife to see me.

DANFORTH HOSPITAL STATISTICS, JULY 1, 1918

Dispensary visits, new	8,818
Dispensary visits, old	8,576
Hospital in-patients	1,142
Operations under anaesthetic	561
Obstetric cases	93
Out-visits	361
Surgical dressings	13,591

Grand total of treatments................ 33,142
Grand total receipts for fees and drugs, $7,701.19 Mex.
Total number of patients who have accepted Christ, 600.

SELECTIONS

From Swatow, China, comes a moving story of the power of a medical mission. A well-to-do Chinese merchant of Swatow, hearing of the good deeds done at the hospital, began, and for a number of years continued to send to the doctor tickets for cash and rice to be given to the poorest of the patients. These would amount sometimes to as much as ninety dollars in the year. He did this with a view to amass merit for himself. He kept a daybook in which he entered his merits and demerits, finding doubtless at the end of the year that there was a large balance to the credit of his meritorious deeds.

He came himself one day to the hospital, and saw the doctor kneeling down and dressing the sores of a poor beggar. "Ah!" he said, "I could not do that; that is too much." Another time he listened to the message given to the patients. It was on the forgiveness of one's enemies, and he ejaculated, "That is beyond me; I could not do that." He found also that the Chinese Christians were really seeking to carry out the teaching and his self-righteousness got a severe blow. He began to be in earnest about his soul, and later on he came into the light. He began also to be in earnest about giving in a still worthier fashion. On one occasion he gave two thousand dollars, and on another, twenty thousand, and once again, six thousand; all in connection with the Swatow medical mission work. He passed through many trials, but held fast his faith, and was baptized in the presence of a great crowd of people.

The woes of Chinese medical treatment bear with special hardships on Chinese women. Their physical miseries are beyond estimate. The presence of an educated Christian medical woman in the sick room, wise and winning, strong and sweet, is one of God's best gifts to China.

Arthur H. Smith.

OUTLINE OF CHAPTER IV.

OUTLINE FOR KOREA

1. *Korea becomes Cho-sen.*
2. *Racial Traits, Religions and Customs.*
3. *Status of Korean Women.*
4. *Native Treatment of Disease.*
5. *Christ comes to Korea.*

OUTLINE FOR THE PHILIPPINES

1. *Where Two Streams meet: Orient and Occident.*
2. *Characteristics of the Filipinos.*
3. *The American Invasion: Political, Religious, Scientific.*
4. *Medical Missions in the Islands.*

OUTLINE FOR SIAM

1. *Obstacles to Missionary Work.*
2. *Results of Medical Missions.*

Work among Lepers in the Far East.

CHAPTER IV.

KOREA, THE PHILIPPINE ISLANDS AND SIAM

"When the modern Korean decides to be a Christian he tells his friends that he has made up his mind to *do the doctrine.*'"

Missionary Review of the World.

In the streets of a town of Korea a stranger stood one morning at an early hour and watched a missionary passing on his way. "Who is that man?" the stranger asked of a Korean.

"He is the Jesus man, going to see some one who is sick," was the reply.

The Jesus men and the Jesus women with their ministry of life and healing are conquering Korea for their King in a deeper sense than the agents of the Japanese Government won it for their Emperor. That Korea is now annexed politically to Japan is, however, undeniably greatly to her own material advantage.

1. Korea becomes Cho-sen

Cho-sen, the old name, meaning land of the morning freshness, has become the new name of Korea as a province of Japan. "From a political point of view the geographical position of this country is most unfortunate. Placed between two rival nations, aliens in blood, temper, and policy, Cho-sen with her twelve millions of population has been the rich grist between the powerful upper and nether millstones of China and Japan with their vast resources. From prehistoric days she has been threatened or devastated by her enemies. Nevertheless, Korea has always remained Korea, a separate country, and the people are Koreans, more allied to the Japanese than the Chinese, yet in language, politics, and social customs different from either."

2. Racial Traits, Religions and Customs

A racial trait of the Koreans most repellent to the foreigner is their unspeakable uncleanliness. All refuse is thrown on the ground and left in the hot sun. Liquid filth is carried in open trenches and left to seep into the soil and contaminate the wells. In the wet season a Korean city becomes a hotbed of cholera, typhus, and like diseases. The Korean, naturally indolent, resents the determined efforts of the usurping Japanese authorities to clean his filthy alleys and inaugurate sanitary measures, but it cannot be denied that, as regards the physical basis of life, the taking over of the reins of power by Japan is all to the good. Korea is rousing to a realization of her abject poverty, ignorance, and backwardness as related to modern civilization; she clamors for enlightment and education. Japan is not only cleaning her up, but waking her up. But another power than that of Japan is *lifting* her up, in the highest sense.

"Human nature in good average quality and quantity dwells under the big hat of the Korean." Indeed, it is a common experience that those who live for any length of time in the Orient come to realize that the difference between the Occidental and the Oriental is largely superficial. The assurance that "God hath made of one blood all the nations of the earth" takes on a new significance and creates quite a different attitude of mind. Missionaries have put the matter to proof by planting the seed that God is Love, not fear, and, behold, in Korea we see a twentieth century Apostolic Church.

The Korean himself. The Korean has been caricatured and usually regarded as contemptible and hopeless. But those who have found the way to his heart reveal another picture. His national traits are lovable ones and among these one of the most sacred is that of hospitality. It is said that this is so marked that inns are very few; houses are so built that the exterior room may provide rest and welcome even for the stranger. His conservatism is obvious from his having remained Korean notwithstanding his menacing environment. Neighborliness, an innate respect for the law of brotherhood which reveals itself in numberless little ways, especially on occasions of need, is very beautiful.

Love of children. The normal Korean is fond of children, especially of sons, who in his eyes are worth ten times as much as daughters. Exposure of children is unknown. Judging from collections of toys, terms of endearment, and words relating to games, sports, festivals and recreations, nursery stories, etc., the life of little Kim must be a pleasant one. While girls are not prized as highly as boys yet they are neither superfluous nor unwelcome. The birth of a girl is not made an occasion of rejoicing, but that of the first-born son is.

There are no separating dialects. The language lends itself to the strongest vituperation, that torrent of vocal filth which flows so freely and characterizes all unrestrained emotion in the Orient. It is said also to surpass English as a medium of public speaking. Literacy is not monopolized by the men. Perhaps two women in five study a little Chinese, but not more than one per cent. really learn to read it.

Buddhism, Confucianism, together with the worship of ancestors, and what we might call Demonism, all have a part to play in the life of Korea, but it is a minor and by no means a vital part, with the exception of the last-named. Korea is unique in that she apparently is a nation without a religion. Travelers find "cities without priests or temples, houses without god shelves, village festivals without idols carried in festive processions, marriage and burial without priestly blessing."

When trouble comes in the form of illness, from palace to hovel the people resort to the sorceress who is supposed to have commerce with evil spirits. She is the lowest of the low, an outcast and yet an indispensable factor in the community. Wherever there is illness the Mu-dang or Sorceress is constantly seen going through various musical and dancing performances in front of the house where the sickness occurs. Millions of dollars are spent annually to support this 'worm eating the heart of this nation unknown.' The name, Mu-dang, means deceiving crowd and no women in Korea are more depraved than she, yet all women and most men fear her and support her nefarious work. Akin to her, yet different, is the blind exorcist, the Pan-Su, who is an

STUDENTS AND STAFF OF PEKING UNION MEDICAL SCHOOL

enemy of the spirits and drives them away by a
superior power. The authority of these charlatans
has been perceptibly on the wane since Christianity
was introduced into Korea.

3. Status of Korean Women

As a class women have greater freedom in Korea
than in some Asiatic countries. In this they resemble the Burmese women. There are three main classes, the upper, middle, and lower, and the better bred
a woman is the greater is her seclusion. With her
literally liberty is peril. The chief business of women
is motherhood. But there are, in addition, other
occupations which they may enter, such as the keeping of a wine shop. This is an occupation for a
woman of the upper class. Silk-culture, tutoring
Chinese classics, keeping of bees, making of straw
shoes, exorcism, fortune-telling, sewing and em-
broidery may occupy her time. But the highest
form of labor to which a lady is eligible is that of a
physician. In fact, no woman can be a physician in
Korea unless she belongs to the upper class. Of the
nature of this medical practice we shall hear more
presently.

"Look here."   Marriage takes place by public recip-
rocal salutation. If the husband re-
pudiates his wife, he cannot take another. The
permanence of the marriage tie is fully recognized,
though fidelity is a feminine virtue. The woman
after marriage drops her given name and is known
as the wife of so and so or the mother of so and so.
Her husband addresses her as "Yabu," meaning

"Look here," which is significant of her relations to him. Silence is regarded as a wife's first duty. Wives among the common people, who are insubordinate, are reduced to order by a good beating, but in the noble class custom forbids a husband to strike his wife.

The seclusion of girls in the parental house is carried on after marriage and in the case of women in the upper and middle classes is as complete as possible. They never go out by daylight except in completely closed chairs, carried by coolies.

Perpetual widowhood is not exacted as in India, yet remarriage is considered improper in the upper classes and grave social disorders arise if the widow does not becomingly weep for the deceased and wear mourning all her days. It often happens that young widows commit suicide in order to prove fidelity and secure honor and reputation beyond the taint of suspicion.

"Domestic life as we know it is unknown," writes Mrs. Bishop. "The women in the inner rooms receive female visitors and the girl children are present. The boys at a very early age are removed to the men's apartments where they learn from the conversation that every man who respects himself must regard women with contempt."

4. *Native Treatment of Disease*

We have already seen the predominant place given to the Sorceress and to the Exorcist in the native treatment of disease in Korea. The invisible spirit of smallpox is ever present to be propitiated and these acts of propitiation play a large part in domestic life, as death from this disease was formerly about equal to the birth rate. The Korean puts smallpox in the forefront of all the ills that flesh is heir to. It is said that he does not count his children until they have had it. It is more feared even than cholera. From the fifth day after the appearance of the disease, no member of the household may comb his hair, or wear new clothes, or sweep the house, or bring any new goods within the doors, cut wood, drive nails, roast beans, or allow a drain to be blocked up. Any one of these would leave the patient blind or seriously marked. The thirteenth day is the one on which the spirit is supposed to depart. On that day the Mu-dang comes and goes through an elaborate ceremony in which she petitions the spirit to deal kindly with the patient and not to leave it pockmarked.

In treating cases of cholera a pair of telescope baskets is used; this disease is supposed to result from rats climbing about in the human interior. The scratching sound made by a peculiar use of the baskets which resembles the noise made by cats is expected to drive away these rodents. Leprosy, typhoid, tuberculosis and diseases which are common with us are found, for the most part, untreated. Baths are infrequent. The air is often polluted by the corpses of the dead lying unburied until the Sorceress shall appoint a propitious time and place for burial. The worst sufferings are caused by the ignorant practices of native physicians. Many native Korean lady physicians administer powdered tiger claws, tincture of bear's gall, or decoction of crow's feet. The steel needle is the unnecessary cause of many blind eyes, and the burning of the body with powder or hot metal to let the demon out has caused many scars on innocent, helpless bodies. If the light that is in them be darkness, how great is that darkness.

When a woman is taken sick, not only is she in trouble but domestic affairs generally are deranged. In the minds of all, this sickness is caused by malignant demons and the people live in constant terror of offending these spirits whose name is legion.

5. Christ comes to Korea

In the year 1883 Korea, the Hermit nation, was opened to the outside world by treaty. The single word *Korea* cabled to Shanghai, early in 1884, declared that the Presbyterian Board of Foreign Missions was ready to begin the work of Christ in this unknown field. "This cablegram was the first voice from Protestant Christendom to molest the age-old heathenism of Korea. It was destined to wake the echoes from end to end of the kingdom." For at Shanghai were waiting Dr. Allen, a young physician, and his wife, ready for the word of command to start upon the *great adventure in Korea*.

Soon after the arrival in Seoul of these missionaries anti-foreign riots broke out, on the occasion of the opening of the first Korean post office, December, 1884. In the days of violence which followed many persons were wounded. With the exception of the medical missionary and his wife, every foreigner fled the city. Intrepid, fearless, Dr. Allen stood his ground. "I came to do just such work," he said. "I can't leave these wounded people. We shall live in the Legation with the old flag flying and trust the kind Father to care for us."

The missionary boldly made his way to the palace and offered his help to the nephew of the King who, under his ministrations, recovered from severe wounds. At once Dr. Allen became the most popular man in Seoul, with the King himself his friend, and a government hospital under royal patronage opened February, 1885, with the missionary in full charge. Within the first year ten thousand patients were treated. Thus did the Battalion of Life take possession of Cho-sen in the Name of the King. The hospital so founded is now merged in the famous Severance Union Hospital, largest and best-equipped in the country.

Doctor to the Queen.   Dr. Scranton, sent by the Methodist Board, arrived in Korea in May, 1885, and a year later Miss Ellers, a medical student and trained nurse under appointment by the Presbyterian Board, won such favor with the Korean Queen that she appointed her royal physician. To Miss Ellers belongs the honor of being the first medical woman to enter the new field. The demand for women physicians, in view of the seclusion of upper and middle class women, becoming imperative, Dr. Allen and Dr. Scranton sent a plea to America which brought ready response. In 1887, the first fully qualified woman physician arrived in Cho-sen in the person of Miss Meta Howard, M.D. She opened in Seoul, in 1888, the first hospital for women in the country. The King showed his approval by sending a name, Po Ku Nyo Kwan, meaning "Saving all women Hospital," painted in the royal colors, framed and ready to hang over the gate. Other women followed, being cordially received by the Government as well as by the women, who came in closed chairs or veiled in their green coats. Dr. Rosetta Sherwood arrived in Korea in 1890, and took up the work laid down through broken health by Dr. Howard. She established the first dispensary for women in the interior of Cho-sen. She was followed, 1893, by Dr. Cutler, and the closing year of the decade following the coming of Dr. Howard was marked by the arrival of seven missionary women physicians.

Such, in briefest outline, were the initial steps in the establishment of women's medical work for women in Korea. At Seoul and at Pyeng Yang are hospitals exclusively for women maintained by the Woman's Foreign Missionary Society of the Methodist Episcopal Church, and there are women physicians on the staff of several of the twenty or more mission hospitals.

Pentecost in Korea.   The story of Protestant missions in Korea is less than thirty-five years old, but, unlike the story in India and China, evangelistic and medical missions developed together,—the word of life and the touch of healing coöperating all the way. We may reasonably ask ourselves whether this fact is not a factor, a potent factor, in the unprecedented power with which the Gospel has made its way into the hearts and lives of these Koreans. Let us grasp clearly the outstanding points and turning points in the wonderful spread of the Evangel.

Dates to remember. In 1884 the seed was first sown. A decade of silent, imperceptible growth followed, at the end of which there were only one hundred and forty Christians in Korea.

In 1894 there was war between China and Japan. Korea was the battleground and like Belgium, in the present decade, it suffered terrible devastation. The missionaries, in the main medical men and women, stood by the people unflinchingly through peril, pestilence, and pain. Hundreds of lives were saved by their devotion and the hearts of the people were deeply touched. "How these foreigners love us! Would we do as much for one of our own kin as they do for strangers?" became the common question. Since the Jesus man had thus proved himself their best friend, his religion must be true, divine.

A Pentecostal revival of Christian religion began then in Korea and has continued from that time, although 1907 was the year of high tide. In 1910 it was said that there had been an average of one convert an hour for every hour of the day since the first missionaries set foot upon Korean soil. All sectarian lines were swept away. The Koreans were simply primitive Christians, not Methodists or Presbyterians. Most significant is the fact that, from the first, the awakening in Korea has been, not a reaching out for Western education and progress, but purely a desire for the religion of Jesus Christ. Almost it can be said that a nation has been born in a day.

"I wish I could tell you how these people change when the Spirit of God comes into their hearts," says Dr. Brown. "You can usually recognize a Korean Christian upon the street by the unmistakable evidences of *cleanliness and a new hope. A visit to Korea is a tonic to faith.*"

* * * * *

In reviewing the story of Christ's work in Korea, curiously pathetic in its humility, its patience of hope, its quiet heroism, two figures stand out as types and symbols; the American physician, Rosetta Sherwood Hall, and her devoted pupil, the beloved Korean physician, Esther Kim Pak. We shall become better acquainted with the latter in Chapter VI. In the year 1890, Dr. Rosetta Sherwood, a graduate of the Woman's Medical College of Pennsylvania, arrived in Seoul to take up the work of the Woman's Hospital and Dispensary, the first in Korea, started by Dr. Meta Howard. The latter had been obliged by ill health to leave Korea during the preceding year. Dr. Sherwood's marriage to Dr. James Hall of the Korean mission took place in 1892, but soon after they were happily settled in their home in Seoul the husband was called upon to depart for the city of Pyeng Yang nearly one hundred and eighty miles north, while his wife stayed at her post in the Woman's Hospital. Here the young Korean girl, Esther, was at once her pupil and interpreter. In 1893, the Doctor began work at Chemulpo among native women, under her influence whole families being won for Christ. In 1894, after the great battle of Pyeng Yang was fought between the Chinese and Japanese, Dr. James Hall, having contracted typhus fever while laboring for the Korean war refugees, returned home to die. His widow, taking with her her two children and the young Korean, Esther Kim Pak, whom she hoped to have educated for a physician, returned to the United States. In her two years at home Dr. Hall devoted herself to study of methods for teaching the blind and upon her return to Seoul, in 1897, the system was perfected, the "New York point" for the blind being adapted to the Korean alphabet. She had embossed the first books before the apparatus arrived from New York. The aim of the school is to fit its members, as rapidly as possible, to share, as is right, in the educational privileges afforded their seeing and hearing brothers and sisters, that together they may earn a livelihood and discharge their duties as loyal and good citizens of the Government General of Cho-sen and of the Kingdom of Heaven, to both of which they belong. The exhibit made by this Blind and Deaf Department received a handsome silver medal from the great industrial exhibition at Seoul.

On the occasion of the Emperor's birthday, Dr. Hall was presented with a nest of silver cups and a certificate for meritorious service in official recognition of her twenty-five years of work in Korea. A literal translation of the certificate is as follows:

From early time you have done not a few noble deeds in regard to education and benevolence and you are, indeed, a good example to the people. Accordingly the Governor General of Cho-sen awards one set of silver cups to you as a token of its appreciation, 31st of October, fourth year of Taisho.

Count Terauchi,
The Governor General of Cho-sen.

This was the first time that a missionary in Korea, man or woman, had been thus honored by the Government.

The Chinese vice-consul, Chang, of Chemulpo, wrote to Dr. Hall in his congratulatory letter that he wished her to succeed upon success, perhaps the most difficult task. Before leaving on furlough Dr. Hall was granted an audience with his Excellency Count Terauchi, the Premier of the Japanese Empire, at his official residence in Tokio. A brief extract officially translated reveals the attitude of this high power in Japan towards Korean women physicians.

His Excellency, Count Terauchi, is very pleased and satisfied to learn that your Korean girls, three in number, have graduated from the government medical school, and are given license to practice medicine without further examination. They will, undoubtedly, not spare their noble efforts for Korean women and children. Their future success is most sincerely hoped for. The people will be happy when many girls follow their example.

Dr. R. Ikebe,
Private Secretary.

The following well-deserved expressions are added to show the official attitude of those in authority at home toward the service of Dr. Hall and of Korean medical women in general. Mrs. John M. Cornell, Honorary Corresponding Secretary of the New York Branch of the Woman's Foreign Missionary Society of the Methodist Episcopal Church, wrote Dr. Hall as she returned on furlough:

I want to sing a doxology with you concerning those three medical graduates with their license to practice already obtained. It surely is worth all the life, energy, prayer and fight that you have given to accomplish this splendid end. As the list grows it seems wonderful. A dozen more already in medical school, a dozen or more preparing, two studying pharmacy, one dentistry, and scores of nurses, actual and preparing. I do not wonder that you come home with a happy heart. You have worked so hard for just this result. May God grant great increase to these years of effort! He knows Korea's need for women workers far better than can any one of the rest of us. He will show you and others how to meet the need financially.

THE PHILIPPINES

"Here is a nation ready to be led to Christ."

Bishop H. C. Stuntz.

The archipelago. The group of islands comprising the Philippine Archipelago number three thousand four hundred and forty-one, one thousand six hundred and sixty-eight of which are listed by name; the others are mere islets. If the map were laid over the United States the islands would extend north and south from Lake Superior to the Gulf of Mexico, east and west a distance a little greater than that from Philadelphia to Indianapolis. Two of the islands are about the size of Pennsylvania, four are about the size of Connecticut, and two about the size of Rhode Island.

Population, language. The population in 1914 was nine million. There are thirty-five languages, nearly a dozen dialects, and sixty-nine sorts of people with heterogeneity raised to its highest power.

Races. There are two main classes of people, the aboriginals and the invaders, or as they are now called, the non-Christian and the

Christianized. Among the latter the type is predominantly Malayan. The only other race really modifying it is the Negrito. Previous to the Spanish conquest these two were the only ethnic sources of the Filipino population. Among the upper and wealthier classes, but embracing but a comparatively small number of individuals out of the entire population, are those having Spanish and Chinese blood in their veins.

1. Where Two Streams meet: Orient and Occident

When the Portuguese discoverers and conquerors reached southeastern Asia, they found a race which called itself Malayan and which in general adhered to the Moslem faith. The Spanish soldiers and missionaries followed with all the hatred for Islam engendered by combating that religion for eight hundred years in Africa and Spain. The Chinese brought the Buddhistic strain and the mingling of the social customs and religions of these peoples has left extraordinary problems.

The ancient religion of the Filipino, known throughout the islands, had no sacred book, but consisted of the *anitos*. These were not gods, they were the souls of the ancestors. Nature spirits, too, were revered; indeed, there was nothing which might not be worshipped. Nine hundred of the gods of the early Filipinos have been counted. They believed that there was one great god called by various names and the rainbow was thought to be his home. It was considered a sin even to point to the rainbow. Old

women acted as priestesses and directed the cere-
monies at marriages and at funerals and tried to
cure the sick. "When a noble died it was the custom
to sacrifice a number of slaves in order that in the
next life the noble should have a suitable retinue
according to the importance of the position he held
while alive. Among some tribes the custom obtained of burying slaves alive."

The Occidental stream of invaders which began
with the Spanish ended with the American. There
are seven main racial and linguistic subdivisions of
the typical Filipino to be found in the Islands and
between them exists more or less suspicion, if not
actual distrust and dislike.

Social orders. There are three classes of society:
the superior, which is composed of
the wealthy families of position, the middle class or
working people, and the dependents. They are not
hedged about by any such caste laws as prevail in
India, though there is a strong line of cleavage between them.

Spanish Catholic. The Spanish occupation and exploita-
tion of the Philippines began in the
first half of the sixteenth century. The Occidental
stream which has been flowing in uninterruptedly
ever since has had abundance of time to reveal its
own character and influence, fruit by which the
tree may be known. But here, as in other countries
where this influence has predominated, dungeons
and scaffolds, closed Bibles and ignorance speak
eloquently.

Priests and Friars. Reformation must be exceedingly
difficult.

The priests and the friars have both been at work during the years of the Spanish regime and some of the priests have accomplished an immense amount of good. . . . While it is by no means true that all of the friars are incompetent or depraved it is, nevertheless, a fact that many of them are ignorant beyond belief; are given over to open and brutal licentiousness; practice inhuman extortion, especially with the solemnization of marriage and the burial of the dead; interfere with the execution of the laws and themselves openly violate them when it serves their ends to do so. The inevitable demoralization of the communities which they control has produced a large class which has suffered at the hands of the friars wrongs that it is not human to forget. (Stuntz.)

2. *Characteristics of the Filipinos*

Writers differ largely in their opinion as to the outstanding characteristics of the people. The individual experience of the writer colors the picture and it is never safe to generalize. The following quotation from Professor Worcester is of value as expressing his own opinion as well as that of a British Consul of Manila: "Rarely is an intratropical people satisfactory to eye or mind, but this cannot be said of the Filipino Malay. In bodily formation and mental characteristics alike he may fairly claim place, not among the middling ones, but among the higher names inscribed on the world's national scale."

The Filipino woman. Spanish civilization found the Filipina woman, as among the Malays, a burden-bearer or a toy. It leaves her the most emancipated woman in Asia. An editorial of the *Manila Bulletin* says: "The Filipino woman is unique among the women of the East in that she is free of foot and face and waist, and stands up and looks straight ahead without fear or confusion."

In this fundamental difference in the social position of woman lies the ground for an abundance of hope for the future Filipino. Her women are modest in demeanor, vivacious in spirit, passionately fond of music, given to hospitality; they have large imitativeness and adaptation and their family affection is strong.

School teachers are unanimous in their opinion of Filipino children. They are docile, quick, mentally alert and have an aptitude for acquiring language. They possess a natural talent for the lesser mechanical arts such as drawing and writing. There is no doubt that they excel American children in docility, imitativeness, and attentiveness. They lack the American child's persistency and originality.

3. The American Invasion: Political, Religious, Scientific

With the American invasion, 1898, came the desired opportunity for the Filipino. Spanish Catholicism not only stood athwart the path of progress, but kept a closed Bible. With the arrival of Protestant Christianity came both Religion and Science. Shiploads of teachers were among the early arrivals. The Census for 1902 reports one hundred and seventy thousand children in primary schools. Under the new influences this number has increased to more than half a million. The changes between the before and after are interesting and numerous.

The open Book. The secret of the greatest change lies in the fact of the open Bible. It is gratifying to know of the confidence which great leaders repose in the value of this book. With the open Bible and the school house came the hospital. The Census of 1902 reported as many as seventy public hospitals in the islands, the whole number of which reported an attendance of only eleven thousand five hundred and fifty-eight patients. The reasons assigned for this small attendance are the expense of maintenance and the prejudice against having the sick cared for away from the family. The latter reason is not borne out by the experience of later years. Before the American occupation, thousands upon thousands were perishing every year for lack of common care. Wounds were covered with chewed tobacco, ashes, and leaves.

Cholera was believed to be caused by a peculiar black dog appearing on the street or by a poison put into wells by Spaniards or foreigners. Cemeteries were not infrequently situated near the supplies of drinking water and conditions within their walls were often shocking. Malaria was common and the stuff on sale called quinine was plaster of Paris or corn starch. Smallpox was generally regarded as a necessary ailment of childhood. It was necessary to forbid by legislation the deliberate communication of it as was commonly done, because it was thought best to have it and be over with it. Children playing with other children were seen to be covered with the eruption. Clothing from people who had died with it was handed down unwashed to other members of the family. The victims often immersed them-

ANOTHER NATIVE AMBULANCE
CHINA

DR. ANNA D. GLOSS, CHINA
President of Woman's Union Medical
School, Peking

selves in cold water when their fever was high and paid the penalty for their ignorance with their lives. Over ten million vaccinations have been made with the result that while previously the annual deaths were about forty thousand, in 1913 there were seven hundred. There is now less smallpox in Manila than there is in Washington.

Bubonic plague. The civil government inherited a well-developed epidemic of bubonic plague. The results of sanitary measures are indicated by the fact that while in 1901 there were four hundred and twenty-seven deaths from this disease there were no cases reported from 1907 to 1912.

Cholera. When an epidemic of cholera broke out and an educative campaign with quarantine regulations was begun, a feeling of bitter hostility was created toward the Board of Health among the native people. Results in the end overbore opposition; from eighteen thousand eight hundred and eleven deaths from cholera in 1908 the report fell to two hundred and three in 1911 and none at all in 1912.

An educational campaign with amazing results combined to nullify the superstitious practices formerly carried on by the Filipinos, and it is now possible safely to count on sufficient co-operation from the people to make an effective campaign possible when next it appears.

Dysentery. This disease, which killed thousands annually, has been reduced to a negligible minimum by simple hygienic measures and a pure water supply. The drinking supply of many provincial towns has been gradually improved by the sinking of artesian wells resulting in a reduction of the death rate by more than fifty per cent. Bishop Oldham writes of seeing an enthusiastic Filipino when first an artesian well shot up a stream of deliciously cold water, four-inches thick and several feet above the ground. First testing the water he stood up and said, "Ah! these Americans! They bring fire out of the sky and water out of the bowels of the earth! They have done more for us in ten years than Spain would have done in a thousand."

Benefit of the Western methods.

At the outset malaria was killing as many people as smallpox. Calapan, the capital of Mindoro, was in Spanish days known as the white man's grave on account of the prevalence of pernicious fever there. Today it is an exceptionally healthy town. Old jails have been rendered sanitary. At Balibio, the annual deaths in 1905 were two hundred and forty-one and fifteen per cent. per thousand. In six months the rate was reduced to seventy per thousand. Careful research revealed the hook worm as the cause, along with other intestinal parasites and the death rate dropped to thirteen per thousand.

At first foreign medical men working in the Far East good naturedly ridiculed all attempts by United States' authorities to make better conditions, claiming that in tropical countries it was customary to take only such steps as would safeguard the health of the European residents. They assured us that it was really best to let the masses live as they would, since Orientals were incapable of sanitary reform. At first, efforts to eliminate Asiatic cholera, leprosy, and plague were viewed with amusement not unmixed with contempt; but the results obtained soon aroused lively interest. Foreign governments began to send representatives to the annual meeting of the Philippine Island Medical Association. Later it became the Far Eastern Association of Tropical Medicine, the biennial meetings of which bring together the most experienced, skilful, and widely known physicians and sanitarians of the East, for an interchange of views and experiences which is invaluable.

A great general hospital has been established. By its side stands a modern, up-to-date college of medicine and surgery. These have been incorporated with the University of the Philippines and members serve interchangeably.

4.   Medical Missions in the Islands

Where among all needy peoples may the Christian women of America have larger scope or a more interesting work than in helping the Filipina woman to help her own people and the people of the neighboring countries? Among the un-Christianized Filipinos the same attitude toward women is found as among the Mohammedans and followers of other Oriental religions, the same inbred fear of demons and spirits, the same low value of human life, the same ignorance and hopelessness which we have found in other countries. Abundant opportunity is offered of accomplishing great things for the uplift of these people. What has been done by the Govern-

ment can also be intensified through the influence
of Christian women. Bishop Oldham says that "the
women of America need not hesitate to make large
investments in the Filipina. She will more than
repay all the care and love that may be extended
. . . . educated young women move freely among
the homes of the people without excessive chaper-
onage; single women, when they are modest and
tactful, are as freely welcomed to the homes as any.
No such freedom as hers is found in Asia."

Within three months from that May Sunday in
1898, when Commodore Dewey broke the Spanish
fleet and entered Manila Bay, Protestant missionary
representatives were on the spot. As a consequence
of consultation held by this advance guard of the
Army of Christ, missionary work was begun in the
following spring under Methodist and Presbyterian
auspices. In January, 1900, Dr. J. Andrew Hall
began medical and evangelistic work at Iloilo on
the island of Panay. The hospital opened by Dr.
Hall is now the Union Missionary Hospital, jointly
sustained by the Presbyterian and Baptist Boards.
Associated with this hospital is a nurses' training
school begun by Dr. Hall and the first of its order
in the Islands.

At Manila notable work is carried on by St.
Luke's Hospital, connected with Bishop Brent's
Mission (Protestant Episcopal) and by the Mary J.
Johnston Memorial Hospital for women and children,
established in 1906 by the Woman's Foreign Mis-
sionary Society of the Methodist Episcopal Church.

Better babies.   Thirty-three per cent. of Filipino
babies die before completing the

first year of life. The causes which lead to this appalling result are being carefully investigated. Popular interest has been aroused, but many years of patient work may be necessary before anything approaching satisfactory results may be brought about. It cannot all be charged to climate. It is a well-known fact that a large number of the Filipina women are unable to nurse their children. As a result, the children begin to eat solid food long before they can digest it, and cholera infantum or convulsions end their lives. It is not difficult to predict the result when babies three or four months old are fed rice, bananas, and mangoes as a regular diet. Dr. Parish in the Mary J. Johnston Hospital has made the slogan for her hospital "better babies." Since 1907, two thousand eight hundred and nine babies have first opened their eyes on life in the hospital. Of the need for such work, she writes in the last annual report:

There are no words to describe the terrible suffering and need among the children; one good thing about the very little and young ones, they can at least die; but the larger children undergo the most terrible diseases and distress, and many times live on and on when there is no hope and nothing in life, apparently, to live for. Dreadful accidents occur, injuries and sicknesses, most of which could be prevented, are all too common . . . . We see many mothers trying their best to do well by their growing children, so we are not by any means discouraged, but rather are we spurred on to work and teach until Filipina motherhood saves Filipino childhood.

A visitor, Mrs. Norma W. Thomas, describing this hospital, says, "There are kindergarten and sewing classes; I never knew that a hospital did so many things, but Dr. Parish says she is trying to make hers a sort of social settlement for the poor neighborhood around it. . . . Last year there was a beautiful Christmas tree on the hospital lawn and six hundred little children were there to see and enjoy it."

Several hospitals under missionary auspices might be enumerated, notably those sustained at Manila and Vigan by the Christian Mission, and that opened in 1908 by the American Board at Davao on the Island of Mindanao, but as there are no distinctively women's missionary hospitals, aside from the Mary J. Johnston Memorial, in the Islands extended study does not come within our limits.

Dispensaries. An interesting extension of medical and religious work is found in the establishment of dispensaries in various centres under the care of a nurse and a Bible woman. The people of the towns have contributed generously to the building and support of these dispensaries and eagerly welcome the clinic and the attention given in the homes. The doctor pays a weekly visit and looks after those who are seriously ill. There are plans for a new school dispensary near the high school in Iloilo where aiready Dr. R. Thomas has large first-aid classes among the students, who number fourteen hundred and come from all parts of the province.

In illustration of the dual service, to body and soul, performed by our Christian hospitals we quote from a letter of Dr. Thomas, of the Union Hospital at Iloilo, under date August 19, 1918.

August 19, 1918. We are rejoicing at the Hospital, because a large number of our nurses have taken a stand for Christ. There are nearly thirty and we thought that a fairly large number were Protestant considering the fact that these girls come from Romanist homes and some have been with us but a short time. But there were about twelve who had not openly confessed Christ or at least that had not joined the church. During the past week those who had already given evidence of loyalty to the Lord and several others who had not been so apparently interested signified their desire to take a stand now and we met seven of them and found them ready. One was not at this meeting, but she had already been talked with. This left only four at present in the school who were not members or openly confessed Christians. At the regular Bible class Sunday night, in an impressive meeting, two of those raised their hands, —and as one of the other two already has expressed her desire to join the church, and is being kept back by her mother, we may say that all but one have now taken a stand. These two who raised their hands last night are opposed by relatives, and they may have to wait before actually joining, but they are converts and may be counted as ready to serve with the rest. The one girl remaining we hope will be reached soon.

It is with great joy that we are now able to present almost a united front in our religious work in the Hospital. We are planning to have a normal class for leaders of personal work classes, and to do definite, purposeful, evangelistic work at the bedside. When this is organized we plan to follow up the work done in the Hospital by sending cards to the pastors in the districts to which outgoing patients will return after illness, in order to have them look them up. This will enable us to help the district churches. We are aware that all such organized evangelistic work is likely to become too mechanical if one is not careful, but forewarned is forearmed, evangelistic work is likely to be too haphazard. There can be no more propitious place to reach the hearts of men than in a hospital where they are being kindly treated.

SIAM

"Your missionaries first brought civilization to our country."
                                    Siamese Prince.

Hemmed in between Burma, which belongs to
British India, and French Indo-China, lies the small
Kingdom of Siam, its territory about equal to that
of Korea and Japan combined, its population esti-
mated as half that of Korea, viz., about six millions.
There is in all Indo-China but one Protestant Mission, that of the Christian and Missionary Alliance;
in Siam the Presbyterian Mission today holds the
field, practically alone.

1.   Obstacles to Missionary Work

This irregular peninsula, counterweight to India,
the two constituting the double pendant of Southern
Asia, seems never to have offered a fertile soil for
the spread of Christianity. Siam is ancient missionary ground. Protestant missions there date back
to the days of the Judsons when the English Baptist Mission press in Serampore printed a Christian
catechism in Siamese (1819). A little later, in answer to the appeal of the famous Dr. Gutzlaff of
the Netherland Missionary Society, the American
Board sent out Rev. David Abeel, and later Messrs.
Johnson and Robinson, who founded a mission in
Bangkok in 1834. This was reinforced by Dr. Daniel
B. Bradley, distinguished preacher and physician,
and a score of other faithful workers. The work was
finally abandoned, as was that of the American
Baptist Missionary Union, begun in 1853. The con-

trolling reason for the withdrawal of these two agencies was that the Siamese people showed little disposition to receive Christianity, and that, as the chief results of missionary work were among the Chinese, it appeared wiser to turn to China itself.

Siamese soil unreceptive. Many reasons, political as well as racial, have combined to render the native Siamese unresponsive to the labors of Protestant missionaries. As national pride restrains the Japanese from adopting the religion of Christ, and as ancestor worship in China and caste in India are formidable barriers, so in Siam is found an all-pervading hostile influence to the Cross, subtle but impervious; it is the indifference, apathy, languor of the tropics, approaching, it might for a time seem, a lack of spiritual capacity. A decadent, idolatrous Buddhism, strongly entrenched in the common life and custom of the people, has constituted in itself a stubborn obstacle to the entrance of new and spiritual conceptions.

Encouragements. As an offset to these discouraging conditions the missionary finds among the Siamese and Lāo (the people of Northern Siam) no caste, no ancestral worship, no child marriage, no seclusion of women.

In no other country of Asia, except Korea, says Dr. Brown,* are Protestant missionaries regarded with greater friendliness by people of all ranks. Their lives and property are as safe as if they were under British rule in India. Princes and nobles are their friends. Men trained in the universities of Europe ask them questions. Missionary educators teach the sons of governors,

---

* See *The Nearer and the Farther East*, by S. M. Zwemer and A. J. Brown, United Study Series, Macmillan, 1908.

judges and high commissioners; and missionary physicians are called into the homes of the proudest officials.

Survival of the Presbyterian mission. We have noted that today the missionaries of the Presbyterian Board alone are at work for the Siamese people. Their persistence in face of bitter suffering and discouragement is meeting its due reward, and they are entering into the fruits of the labors of their brethren of other communions but like faith, for we may firmly believe that no effort made in the Name above every name has been lost.

Permanent work was established by the Presbyterian Board in Bangkok in 1849 by two missionaries, the Rev. S. Mattoon and Dr. S. R. House. The latter continued in active service for twenty-nine years. As Dr. Bradley remained at his post after the withdrawal of its missionaries by the American Board in 1849, and continued his work until his death at Bangkok in 1873, it can fairly be said of Siam as of Korea, that Christian work of permanence there has, from the first, been medical as well as evangelistic.

Apostles of Christian civilization. Dr. Bradley was a man of varied and unusual gifts and made a deep impression upon the Siamese, as did his co-worker, the Rev. Jesse Caswell. The latter, chosen by Siam's king as tutor to his son and heir, inculcated in the youth (who became the truly enlightened and progressive King Mongkut) the principles which have opened the land to civilization. Dr. Bradley in the year 1836 introduced the printing press and in 1840 met the terrible national scourge of smallpox by the introduction of vaccination.

2. Results of Medical Missions

During the first critical years of the Mission, the medical work was the chief means of allaying the natural prejudices against the foreigners and gaining toleration from the old king. His son, who came to the throne in 1868, was educated under missionary influence, and desired to obtain for his people the benefits of scientific medical practice. In this endeavor the American missionary physicians were his trusted advisers. With their aid, he established in Bangkok hospitals for the army and navy, two general hospitals, an insane asylum and a Royal School of Medicine. All the mission hospitals were indebted to him for generous gifts of land and buildings. The present king, who was educated in England, continues his father's liberal policy. With the gradual increase of intelligence the new generation has come to recognize, to some extent, the efficiency of modern methods and especially the benefit of surgical skill. But the spread of Western ideas is confined as yet to a very narrow circle, and the masses of the people, both in city and country, are content to live and die in the unsanitary traditions of their forefathers.

Medical work has been in truth the missionary magnet from the first. In 1884 a hospital, founded by the Mission at Petchaburi, was enlarged by the reigning King and somewhat later a women's ward added by the Queen. Since then, five mission hospitals and an equal number of dispensaries have been established, all performing beneficent work, all self-supporting. A free hand has been given the

missionary physicians in their Christian propaganda
by King, Queen, and Government; missionary women
are permitted to enter the royal harem and teach,
and members of the reigning house say without
reserve or condition, "The missionaries first brought
civilization to our country."

Medical work was begun among the Lāo in 1875,
at the important city of Chieng Mai; in 1878, the
King issued a "Proclamation of Religious Liberty
for the Lāo." The original hospital at Chieng Mai
was erected by Dr. McGilvary and Dr. Cheek,
about 1888. In recent years it has been much enlarged, and has now in its spacious compound accommodations for at least fifty patients, besides a chapel
and two physicians' houses. "Since it was practically
impossible to obtain potent vaccine lymph in the
North owing to its isolation, in 1904, Dr. McKean,
who joined this mission in 1890, established a vaccine laboratory and this has supplied lymph to all
the mission stations and to the Government. A
large corps of Christian men are employed to travel
through the province, vaccinating, selling quinine,
and distributing Gospels and tracts. The small fees
received pay their expenses and help to support the
hospital. These men are required to spend three
days each month at the hospital for instruction,
and some of them become very skilful in the use of
simple remedies. They have done excellent work in
combatting the epidemic of malignant malaria.

The hospital is greatly blessed in three native
assistants of long experience. Of the steward and
head nurse, Dr. McKean says: "His whole life and

thought seem given to the service of God. Faithful to every duty, constant, kind and unselfish in the care of our poor sufferers, I verily believe Ai Keo has done more for his own people than any Lāo man that ever lived."

The Overbrook Memorial Hospital at Chieng Mai was built in 1912 on modern lines and has wards for women and children. In all five hospitals and twenty-five dispensaries are sustained by the Mission among the Lāo.

While there are no distinctively women's hospitals in Siam and, up to the present time, no qualified women physicians at work there, a great work for the native women and children has been begun; upon whom does its development rest if not upon ourselves? "Behold, I have set before thee an open door."

WORK AMONG LEPERS IN THE FAR EAST

"In all the long procession of the ages there is no more truly tragic figure than that of the leper."

Leprosy is common in every town east of the Suez Canal; Siam is no exception, nor are Korea and the Philippine Islands. The treatment of lepers in these countries and in others by the Battalion of Life can best be considered at this point. Through the long ages no hand but the hand of the Lord Jesus was stretched out to cleanse and to restore the leper, and it is only when His disciples enter that compassion comes to such as these. They are "cast out by all men, forsaken, despised and unclean, and, according to Buddhist teaching, without a spark of merit or hope of a better future. According to Buddhist belief, they are suffering for sins committed in a previous state of existence, and Buddhism can never be expected to offer them relief. Such relief must come from us who enjoy the blessings of health and home and a Christian civilization."

Leper work in Siam.   From time immemorial the leper in Buddhistic Siam has been indeed hated, feared, brutally treated. At Chieng Mai, Dr. McKean of the Presbyterian Hospital, by the grace of God, was the means, as the second decade of the twentieth century opened, of introducing measures of relief and consolation for these children of despair.

From the admirable sketch of W. M. Danner, secretary of the interdenominational society, "The Mission to Lepers," we condense the following brief account of this typical work:

Half an island in the river, five miles south of Chieng Mai, was the overgrown jungle used as a playground for the Governor's pet elephant. His father, the late Lāo King, had presented him with this "Good Luck" elephant when he came of age. In spite of the fact that he was a pet, he was a wilful, vicious creature. If hungry for rice, he would tear down a granary and help himself. He even demolished native houses to get baskets of rice he knew were there. Unable to endure his raids, the people fled, leaving the elephant monarch of all he surveyed.

Of course, no one could kill a "Good Luck" elephant. But, when the elephant died, Dr. J. W.

McKean hastened to ask the late Governor to devote this island to a higher use; and as a result, half the island, one hundred and sixty acres of land, was donated, on which to establish the first leper asylum in the kingdom; and the gift was confirmed by royal authority in Bangkok.

Even the Siamese began to be interested. One Trading Company made a generous donation of teak logs; another merchant furnished the use of his elephants for hauling; a friend contributed office and photographic help; a girls' school in Chieng Mai made fifty garments for the use of the first patients. Through the aid given by the Mission to Lepers and good personal friends in the U. S. A., Dr. McKean joyfully wrote, "On June 11, 1913, we were rejoiced to formally open the Chieng Mai Leper Asylum, with one hundred patients."

The buildings comprise seven brick cottages, each costing nearly two thousand dollars and built to accommodate twenty persons, with fireplace and sleeping and cooking accommodations, and all sanitary, so that by hose and concrete drains the house can be thoroughly cleansed. In addition, there is a super-intendent's house, a brick water tower, with pumping engine, and a temporary thatched chapel.

Of the one hundred patients in the Asylum on opening day, sixty-five were men. The ages vary from twenty to forty years. There are five untainted children of leper parents. The dread of the disease renders it difficult to place the children in the homes of the people, and a home for untainted children has been established on the island, where they are kept free from contagion, and are yet near enough to their parents for occasional visits.

It is known to all that material benefits have come to Siam with the advent of the missionary, and they have very greatly commended Christianity to the nation. We have a right to hope that once the practical benefits of an asylum are seen by the

Siamese, the Government will take up segregation of the leper on its own account, and Siam may be the first of Oriental nations to rid herself of the scourge.

In the Asylum family there are lepers from Yunnan and from the British Shan States. It is now possible to supply them with medicines and an abundance of good food and clothing, so that, in spite of their terrible sufferings and their hopeless prospects for the future, they are measurably happy. The death rate is approximately ten per cent. each year. All bodies of patients dying of leprosy are cremated.

Nine lepers came over the mountains not long ago, traveling through uninhabited jungles for thirteen days, destitute of money and almost destitute of food. They were a sad and weary company when they came to the Asylum gate in the evening, so glad to find a place of refuge. Within another month, eight more came from the same province, having traveled twelve days. A grandmother brought three leper grandchildren a journey of ten nights. The fiftieth leper came to the Asylum from a village thirteen days distant. It took him a month of travel. There is one family of five, all lepers, in the Asylum.

When the work began at Chieng Mai, Dr. and Mrs. McKean committed to God the future of the Asylum and asked all contributors to its support and all Christian friends everywhere to pray that every leper who should ever come to this Asylum might become a true child of God. These prayers have been answered in a most wonderful manner, for of the two hundred and seventy-four lepers who have found refuge there all have become Christians except one, who came in a dying condition.

In 1914 there was a voluntary contribution by the Chieng Mai lepers to the American Bible Society. This gift was forwarded to the Bible Society with a letter in the following language: "We, the elders and members of the Leper Church at Chieng Mai, with one heart and mind, have great gladness in sending our small offering to the American Bible Society, and we beg that our gift of twenty-five rupees ($8.09) may be graciously received by you

DR. LI-BI-CU, NGUCHENG, CHINA
(By permission of the Woman's Foreign Missionary Society,
Methodist Episcopal Church)

and used for the distribution of the Holy Scriptures. To have a share in this good work will give us very great happiness.

"(Signed) Elders—Peang, Toon, Gnok."

Dr. Robert E. Speer says: "The morning that we were at the Chieng Mai, Siam, Leper Asylum, twenty lepers were baptized and welcomed to the Lord's table. I think the highest honor I have ever had in my life was to be allowed to hold the baptismal bowl out of which these lepers were baptized. I am taking it home as a priceless memorial."

Leper work in the Philippines. The United States Government has set apart the beautiful island of Culion in Manila Bay as a leper colony. There are four thousand, four hundred and forty-four acknowledged lepers in the Philippine Islands; the Culion Colony is the largest in the world, numbering thirty-seven hundred. While the sufferers are in the main Roman Catholics, there has been an appeal for Protestant teaching and now regular visits by missionaries to Culion are sustained and the devoted service of the Bible woman, Sister Juano Coronel and the native pastor, Garchalion, have proved of marked value.

The settlement on Culion is not only the largest, but the most thoroughly and scientifically organized of existing leper colonies. A flourishing town has grown up with good roads, water and sewerage systems, and comfortable homes. Wholesome occupation and entertainment are furnished and all possible measures are taken to render life tolerable to these most afflicted of the race.

Leper work in Korea. There are three leper asylums in Korea. Of peculiar interest is the origin of that at Kwangju, known as the Kwangju Leper Home and presided over by Dr. R. M. Wilson of the Southern Presbyterian Mission: A medical missionary, Dr. W. H. Forsythe, was riding one day toward Kwangju, when he heard a strange noise by the roadside. Dismounting, he found in the bushes a poor leper woman almost dead. Knowing that she would die if he left her, he put her on his own horse and took her to Kwangju. Then this modern Good Samaritan realized that no inn would receive her, neither could any home. With other missionaries, he arranged an unused tile kiln suitably, and fed and taught this poor creature. She welcomed the comfort of the Gospel and accepted the Saviour.

In the meantime, the missionaries among themselves gave funds to build a small three-room house, and here five or six other patients who had heard of the Christian treatment of a leper were cared for. It was now imperative that larger provision be made, and through The Mission to Lepers and the prayers of friends this Macedonian call was answered and the present asylum was created.

Dr. Wilson, the missionary in charge, says:

Donors can never regret their gifts, if they stop to think what a home like ours means to the lepers. A welcome (the first shock), a warm bath (the second shock), clean clothes, a nice Korean room, plenty of bedding, food for each meal, the best medical treatment for their disease, work to do if able, books to read, teaching, the Gospel Story lovingly told, and finally, a Christian burial.

November 15, 1912, was a happy day when we dedicated the Kwangju Leper Home to the Lord. On opening day, twenty-one half-clad, shivering lepers gathered at our dispensary, and, when welcomed to this new home, their worn, haggard faces actually changed to happy-looking countenances. At 3 P. M. all the missionaries and many native Christians gathered, and with songs of praise, prayers of thanksgiving, Scripture readings, and addresses, the Kwangju Leper Home was opened in the name of Him who said "Cleanse the lepers."

In concluding the chapter it remains for us to broaden our vision and survey for a moment the beginnings of work among the lepers of the world, with certain impressive illustrations of the Divine benediction upon this sacrificial service.

First leper hospital. Christ's work for lepers through his latter day disciples begins with William Carey, the founder of modern Protestant Missions, who after witnessing, in 1812, the awful sight of the burning alive of a leper at Calcutta was instrumental in establishing in that city the first known hospital for lepers. In 1822 Moravian missionaries began work among the lepers of South Africa and in 1867 they consecrated their "Jesus Hilfe," the Home for Lepers at Jerusalem. "The Mission to Lepers in India and the East" was formed by Wellesley C. Bailey, an American Presbyterian in the Punjab, India, in 1874. The title of this organization defines its generous scope. Most touching is it to read of the first leper woman to come for succor to this Mission; she had begged her way, traveling to Almora with her two little children, ninety miles from the Himalayas. From the first, provision was made for the separate care and upbringing of untainted children of lepers.

It should be kept in mind that both Hindu and Mohammedan in India regard leprosy as a just punishment for unpardonable sin against a God whose judgment cannot be turned aside. The leper is, therefore, outcast alike from Divine and human compassion.

Work in India. The officials of the Society organized by Mr. Bailey consider five hundred thousand as a conservative estimate of the number of lepers in India. One of the oldest, if not the oldest asylum is that at Almora, North India, founded by the London Missionary Society in 1849. Under the Gossner Mission, founded in 1844, a leper asylum was opened in 1888 at Purulia, where now the largest work of this nature in all British India is conducted. Here is found a model village on a tract of fifty acres of evergreen woods with many spacious dwellings, hospital, dispensaries, and church. One who was cared for in this famous institution, and who has been characterized as "a leper saint" wrote to a distant friend the following letter, impossible to read without deep emotion:

Lady, peace! Your love-heart is so great that it reached this leper village—reached this very place. I, being Guoi Aing, have received from you a bed's wadded quilt. In coldest weather, covered at night, my body will have warmth, will have gladness. Alas, the wideness of the world prevents us seeing each other face to face, but wait until the last day, when with the Lord we meet together in heaven's clouds—then, what else can I utter, but a whole-hearted mouthful of thanks? You will want to know what my body is like—there is no wellness in it. No feet, no hands, no sight, no feeling; outside body greatly distressed, but inside heart is greatest peace, for the inside heart has hopes. What hopes? Hopes of everlasting blessedness, because of God's love and because of the Saviour's grace. These words are from Guoi Aing's mouth. The honorable pencil-person is Dian Sister.

Impossible as it is to extend this review of Christ's work among lepers, since an entire volume would not suffice, let us close with mention of two Christian women who have devoted themselves single-hearted and single-handed to this labor: Miss Riddell, an Englishwoman, who in 1895 opened the Hospital of the Resurrection of Hope in Kumamoto, Japan, for the leprous poor, and Mary Reed, who in 1892, on a Himalayan crest, at Chandag, sixty-four hundred feet above sea level, presented herself to a company of segregated lepers living in huts and stables, as having been set apart by the call of God within to minister to them.

The story of Miss Riddell has been recently given in a study book* of this series and, therefore, does not need repetition here. The story of Mary Reed† has long been familiar in its general outlines, but it is believed that faith and love and pity will stir to quicker life within us, by reading a few passages from letters intimately concerning her and reviewing thus her ministry of compassion.

---

* *World Missions and World Peace*, p. 211ff. By Caroline Atwater Mason, 1916.

† *Mary Reed, Missionary to the Lepers*, by John Jackson, Fleming H. Revell Company.

Early in January, 1892, Mr. Wellesley C. Bailey, Secretary and Superintendent of the *Mission to Lepers in India and the East*, received a letter from Miss Budden, daughter of the well-known London missionary who founded the large leper asylum in Almora, which ran as follows:

I have been expecting to hear from you about the future arrangements for Miss Reed, who has come for shelter to Pithora as being the only place in the world that would shelter her. You will have heard that Miss Reed was for five years in this country as a missionary of the Woman's Foreign Missionary Society of the Methodist Episcopal Church, and went home in utterly broken health. It seems now that this complaint (leprosy), was coming on for some time before she left, and for a year after she arrived in America it was not suspected. At last the Lord Himself revealed it to her, and at the same time told her that Pithora was to be her future home, and that He had much work for her to do among those similarly afflicted. She informed the doctors of the nature of her complaint, and was sent by her own physician to see an expert in New York who confirmed her suspicions, and she was hurried out of the country before others were made aware of her complaint. She saw doctors in London and in Bombay—the doctor of the Leprosy Commission in the latter place—and all agreed that there was no doubt about the matter.

Miss Reed feels that she has had her life call to work among these poor creatures, and, I believe, will end her days among them.

As a result of this appeal, Mr. Bailey was able to appoint Miss Reed to the work to which she had dedicated herself. One of Miss Reed's earliest visitors, the Rev. G. M. Bullock, L.M.S., gives us a glimpse of her in her chosen occupation.

We reached Chandag Heights early on Friday morning and found dear Miss Reed busy in the hospital, tending three patients in a much advanced stage of leprosy. She was binding up, with her own hands, the terrible wounds, and speaking soothing words of comfort to these poor distressed ones. It has always been a trial to her to witness suffering in others, yet she is most devoted in her attentions, and so gentle and kind. We were very much surprised and pleased to find her so active and cheerful, and looking so well. She told us she had never felt better in health, more cheerful in spirits, nor happier in service than she does now. . . . [This is] not the result of any medical treatment she has adopted, as she gave up all treatment of that sort under a strong sense that God only required of her faith in Him and in His healing power.

The Christmas of 1896 brought to the lonely woman in her Himalayan refuge the joy of a visit from one of her closest friends, Dr. Martha Sheldon,* medical missionary from Bhot. The day was spent "on the heights" in every sense by these two intrepid fellow-soldiers of Jesus Christ.

What an evening we had together, wrote Dr. Sheldon later. Christmas morning we were up bright and early, as it was to be a full day. As I walked with Miss Reed to the chapel, I realized the exquisite beauty and adaptability of the location. She has, as Mr. Bailey expresses it, "the whole side of a mountain," and nature is not niggardly here. Those who are accustomed to look upon Miss Reed's work from a purely sentimental standpoint, do not realize the practical and permanent character it bears. The asylum for lepers which, formerly, had been all in one, has now been divided, and new houses for the men and boys built on another and separate portion of the estate. To this locality we went. The rows of neat, well-built houses, with many a green, well-kept garden patch, cultivated by the inmates, ninety in number as an average, presented a pretty sight. The chapel has been built this year. It is commodious and convenient.

---

*See p. 31.

A few glowing sentences from one of Miss Reed's own letters will aptly close this Christmas chapter. "Yesterday," she writes, "we had the most blessed of the five Christmas Days I have spent in this work and in this much-loved home of His choosing. Never was the meaning of that wonderful word *Immanuel* more consciously realized than during this Christmastide."

So we leave Mary Reed. Verily she shall see of the travail of her soul and shall be satisfied.

A NOTABLE CHRISTIAN DOCTOR OF BURMA
MA SAU SA, F.R.C.S.,
Dufferin Hospital, Rangoon, Burma

CHAPTER V.

OUTLINE ON THE NEAR EAST

1. *Persia.*
2. *Arabia.*
3. *Turkey and Syria.*
4. *Egypt.*

CHAPTER V.

THE NEAR EAST

"In every place to which the Cross has gone it has turned the desert into a garden; in every place to which the Crescent has gone it has turned the garden into a desert."

Percy Dearmer.

FROM the Himalayan heights let us imagine ourselves entering one of the many airplanes about to be dedicated to the pursuits of peace. When we have soared above the highest snowpeaks and have hovered for a moment above the "roof of the world," we will steer a straight course west. The Far East is left behind us. Without pausing to alight within the mysterious borders of Afghanistan, still *terra incognita* to our Battalion of Life, we speed on to the Near East, towards the Moslem lands of Persia, Arabia, Turkey, Syria, Palestine. Far off to the southwest looms vaguely Africa's prodigious peninsula.

Islam.   Until we penetrate into Africa beyond the trail of the traders we shall encounter among the peoples who throng these ancient lands chiefly followers of Mohammed. We have known Islam in India, where it prevails, but does not dominate. As we approach the cradle of the Prophet, and enter the regions which came under his sway in his first twenty years of conquest, previous to the middle of the seventh century, and which remain still

under that sway, we wonder if we shall not find
Islam, after all, a better religion than those more
ancient systems which rule the Far East. At least,
we reflect, the Mohammedan is neither heathen nor
idolatrous. He worships one God, and makes unto
himself no graven image.

1. *Persia*

We are flying over Persia now, the land of roses
and nightingales, of Zoroaster and Omar Khayyam,
of mystic legend and lore. Below us now we distinguish, embosomed in rich foliage, the white
minarets, walls, and domes of a large city. Consulting our aerial chart we discover that this city is
Teheran, the Persian capital. Here we will alight,
leaving the airplane to go its way on other errands
for other explorers. We will look about us now and
see with our own eyes what thirteen hundred years
of Moslem domination have done for Persia.

Disenchant-   We find our way through the streets;
ment.   they are but alleys, dark, labyrin-
thine, ominous. We see big-bodied men clad in
white, white turbans on their heads. They walk
past with arrogant stride; occasionally women by
twos and threes, veiled closely save for the eyes,
hasten by in furtive fashion as if to make themselves
invisible as swiftly as possible. The faces of the men
are sensual; the eyes of the women flash sidelong
glances. We look into the dwelling places of the
people, homes no one could term them, human
rabbit-warrens they have been called. Darkness and
dirt reign supreme; squalor, vermin, miserableness
are everywhere. The children huddle together among

pigs and chickens, sitting listlessly on the bare ground while flies, which they are too lethargic to note, swarm over their faces; older boys and girls are busily at work collecting cow and camel dung in baskets. This is taken home, made into flat cakes, and placed upon the house walls to dry both for poultices in case of sickness and for fuel. Little wonder that the atmosphere reeks with pollution. Where are the roses and nightingales of Omar? Instead of liquid bird notes the air shrills with sharp voices of women berating their children in phrases so violent and obscene that we are glad of the limitations of our knowledge of the language.

Persian ladies of fashion. Perhaps, however, we are invited to enter some inner courtyard of a home of wealth and pretension. Here we shall indeed find roses, a fountain, and gaily dressed ladies. We might fancy, from the distance, that these resemble the *houris* of song and story. The illusion fades on nearer view. These Persian ladies loll on low divans, smoking endless cigarettes, sipping endless coffee, devouring sweets and fruit like greedy children, gossiping freely and casually of immoralities the grossest, dozing, quarreling. They do not think; they cannot read; they cannot go abroad at will. If their children are sick they call for some witch-like crone who administers herbs and leeches, or gashes the baby's back with a knife at so much a cut. Perhaps the priest may write a verse from the Koran to be used as a charm against the demon. If death comes to those whom they love they know only despair which finds vent in wild shrieks and hopeless wailing.

Sadly we must admit that the social standards of Islam are no better and the life of the Moslem woman on Moslem ground no whit nobler than in the Far East. Islam is ever the same and ever evil. Listen for a moment to a few expressions of conviction spoken by experts on the ground:

The Moslem Bible (the Koran) perpetuates slavery, polygamy, divorce, religious intolerance, the seclusion and degradation of women; it petrifies social life.

Mohammedanism is corrupt to the very core. The morals of Mohammedan countries are corrupt and the imagination very wicked. Women are degraded with an infinite degradation.

I think Islam has the most blighting, withering, degrading influence of any false creed.

The follower of the Prophet would sooner lie than tell the truth; the whole routine of Moslem life is filled with dishonesty and double-dealing.

The very strongholds of religion are strongholds of immorality in the Moslem world. Slavery, cruelty, contempt of human life, fanaticism are fundamentals.

Woman is held to be a scandal and a slave, a drudge and a disgrace, a temptation and a terror, a blemish and a burden.

A system that puts God's sanction on polygamy, concubinage and unlimited divorce,—that hellish trinity,—brings a curse on every home in the Moslem world by degrading manhood. But these social and domestic evils cannot be rebuked or deplored by better class Mohammedans without reflecting on the career of Mohammed and without contradicting the teachings of the Koran, to them the revealed word of God.

The picture is dark, indeed. Where is light? It is in the Gospel of Jesus Christ. And yet that light hitherto has burned feebly and with a flickering flame in Moslem lands. To change the figure, Islam has stood as the "Gibraltar of Heathendom," the frowning rock of fierce, vengeful bigotry, against which the waves of the incoming tide of Christianity beat almost in vain.

Hope and light. Here in Persia, missionary work, begun in 1834 by the American Board and now carried on, in the main, by the Presbyterian Board, has been forced to address itself largely to the Nestorian and Armenian elements, the Moslem people presenting everywhere an almost solid front of contemptuous opposition; indeed, the death penalty is the price, according to law, of apostasy from the state church of Islam. Humanly speaking, the day would have been lost had it not been for the reinforcement of the Battalion of Life. *The Christian doctor has saved the day*. "All the vast, unoccupied territory in the Mohammedan world," says Dr. Zwemer, "is waiting for the pioneer medical missionary, man or woman. . . . There was a day when Mohammedan fathers and mothers would rather see their children die in their arms than carried to the hospital of the Christian; today every hospital is crowded."

"I can bear my testimony," said the author of *Twenty-five Years in Persia*, "that everywhere, and certainly in Mohammedan lands, the Medical Missions are the keystone of the great missionary arch. They are the key, the only key, which can open the Mohammedan lock."

In 1912, after a visit to Moslem lands, the Bishop of London declared:

"The fact which emerges from a visit to the Near East is the wonderful influence of Medical Missions . . . . As far as I could see the most influential people in the Near East were the Christian doctors."

Mission in Teheran.
Missions here in Persia entered upon a new day when medical work began in Urumia in 1878 under that distinguished pioneer, Dr. Joseph P. Cochran.

But we are still in Teheran. We have seen the dark side of the Moslem city. Let us make our way now to the Central Mission Compound, emerging thus from the sinister atmosphere of lust and filth and cruelty into the fair light of a Christian household. Two miles away, in the north-eastern part of the city, stands the mission's hospital. Land for it was presented by the Persian Prime Minister, whom Dr. W. W. Torrence (it was he who in 1881 began medical work here) cured of an obstinate malady. The hospital was built in 1892, and a new dispensary added in 1893, where during the cholera epidemic of that year more than two thousand patients were treated. During a more terrible season of cholera, in 1904, the missionaries carried on four centres of medical work, in which more than four thousand patients were treated gratuitously.

A Persian lady of highest rank, writes Dr. J. Richter, the wife of a major-general, a relative of the ruling Shah, was operated upon, with the Shah's consent. This proof of confidence on the part of the leading authorities made a deep impression on the population of the capital. From that day women thronged to the hospital as patients. In the same year a wealthy Persian woman gave the money for an addition to the men's hospital, for the special use of poor women. She paid the cost of furnishing the building also, and took a lively interest in the patients, particularly in the severe surgical cases, for which nothing could have been done without a hospital.

This women's building is in charge of Dr. Mary J. Smith, in whom is found an untiring worker not

DR. IDA S. SCUDDER, VELLORE, INDIA
President of the Union Medical School, South India

only in dispensary and hospital, but in the homes
of the purdah women of Teheran. In Persia, as
everywhere in medical missions, the dispensary has
a large part to play in spreading the good news of
the Kingdom.

A dispensary   It is through this agency that Persian
Christian.   women are most widely and effective-
ly reached. An instance in point is given us by an
English observer as occurring near Ispahan, a city
in this part of Persia. A suffering woman, who
came habitually to the Missionary Society's dispensary for treatment, was accompanied by her
niece, an intensely bigoted young Moslem woman,
named Sakineh. After a time the niece was sent
alone to procure medicine for her aunt and found
herself embarrassed by the necessity of hearing
prayer and Bible lesson before the medicine would
be given her. In various ways she tried to get the
bottle without the Christian message, but in vain.
Gradually the words of Divine love touched her
heart; Sakineh listened and believed. With great
courage she renounced Islam completely, declaring
her faith in Jesus as her only Saviour. For two
years she was kept in close confinement, forbidden
all communication with the missionaries; fierce
persecution was visited upon her, from which she
scarcely escaped with her life, but through all these
fiery trials Sakineh remained true. There are many
Sakinehs, perhaps never known by name even to
those through whose lips they heard the Gospel.

General survey.   As we stand in Teheran and look
                  westward over Persia we hail from
afar other outposts of our beneficent Battalion. At

Tabriz there is not only a general hospital, but a hospital for women and children; this was opened in 1899 by Dr. Mary Bradford, who was succeeded by Dr. Edna Orcutt and Dr. Mary R. Fleming. The work is promoted by the ladies of the station who spend much time in visiting lepers and in relief work for refugees. At Hamadan stands the Lillie Reed Holt Memorial, the only hospital between Teheran and Bagdad, a distance of five hundred miles. Here we find a separate women's hospital, the Whipple Memorial, in charge of Dr. Mary Allen. At Urumia, head centre of the Persian Mission, is the famous Westminster Hospital, built in 1880, during the life of the lamented Dr. Cochran. Howard Annex for women was added in 1890. This is the largest and most thoroughly equipped hospital in Persia and its success has been such as to break down the almost invulnerable wall of Moslem prejudice. Followers of the Prophet no longer hesitate to imperil their hope of paradise by sleeping under a Christian roof, eating Christian food, taking Christian medicine, and submitting to the defiling touch of Christian hands. This betokens a new day for Persia. Truly, the mainspring of missionary effectiveness in these regions is found in the medical work. The Gospel, diligently preached in the hospital wards, faithfully distributed by means of printed portions in the dispensaries, has been heard with gladness and received with many hopeful signs. Despite the terror and confusion which ruled for a time in the war zone, the report of Urumia for 1918 declares, "The past year every department, evangelistic, educational, and medical, has been in

operation. . . . The medical work has ministered
to people of every class, as has been the case during
the whole history of the mission." This favorable
report from the Persian mission storm centre of war
perils gives the keynote for the others. Unrest,
however, is not at an end.

We have, coming to our hospitals and dispensaries, people of
many nationalities, obtaining relief from their sufferings and
being brought under the sound of the Gospel. The Medical
Mission work helps every other branch of the work; we have
sometimes found it extremely difficult to get congregations on
Sunday morning to our Persian services where we have no
hospital, but, where we have medical work established, there we
have literally hundreds of Mohammedans at the services. In
Ispahan, where we used to have a mere sprinkling of Mohammedans on Sunday morning, now we have week after week one
hundred and seventy to two hundred Persians in the church.
At the Christmas and Easter festivals we sometimes have six
hundred to eight hundred Mohammedans in church, with an
overflow of one hundred and thirty to one hundred and eighty
in another building. If it were not for Medical Missions we
should not get these congregations in our churches.

At the same time the Medical Mission is helping the schools.
Where we used to have great opposition from Mohammedan
mullahs, our schools constantly closed, parents fined, teachers
beaten, pupils driven away, we have now men and women doctors,
men's and women's hospitals, and the mullahs say, "The doctors
are our best friends. What are we to do with our wives and
daughters if in time of sickness they have no hospital to go to?"
The consequence is, they look at the schools and say, "We had
better not interfere with them. The doctor and clergyman and

schoolmaster are working together. We shall find them our best friends, and therefore we had better let the pupils continue at their studies." Not only these congregations on Sunday are themselves very largely due to the work of Medical Missions, but the fact that we have hundreds of boys and girls in our schools is also largely due to the work of Medical Missions.

Bishop Stileman, author of

Twenty-five Years in Persia.

2.   *Arabia*

"There are certain fields of missionary endeavor where medical missions appear destined to exert a peculiarly powerful influence. This would seem to be especially true in Mohammedan countries."

J. R. Williamson.

Mohammed, the Prophet of Islam, its head and founder, was born at Mecca and died at Medina, cities of Arabia. In the year 632 A. D., the date of Mohammed's death, it is believed, not a Christian was left alive in Arabia. *"From that date,"* says Dr. A. J. Brown (the italics are his), *"until the day of Keith Falconer, the whole of Arabia was utterly, continuously, and inexplicably neglected by the Church of Christ in its work of evangelization. The false prophet held undisputed sway over the whole peninsula."* It was in 1885 that Keith Falconer and his wife, self-supporting missionaries, went to Aden. Since his death, which followed in but a few months, the Free Church of Scotland has carried on the work in Aden, in particular the hospital.

Mission work in Arabia is further carried on by the Reformed Church in America under whose auspices the Arabian Mission was organized in 1889,

Dr. James Cantine and Dr. Samuel M. Zwemer having been the pioneer missionaries. The centres are at Bahrein, Busrah, Muscat, and Kuweit. At all these stations medical work is in charge of a staff of ten physicians, six men and four women. Many thousand patients, men, women, and children, have been treated in hospital and dispensary practice yearly with gratifying results.

The history of the medical work has been one of extension and growth, of gradual increase in the force of workers, and occupation of new fields. In 1900, work was definitely opened at Bahrein, and in October, 1902, the new Mason Memorial Hospital was taken into use, and formally dedicated at the Mission Meeting in January, 1903. In Busrah, meanwhile, a large work continued to be carried on, but with no accommodations for in-patients, surgical and medical, beyond those furnished by a commodious native house. The spring of 1910, however, saw the laying of the cornerstone of the Lansing Memorial Hospital, and the building went rapidly on to completion the same year. The previous year, 1909, a doctor was established at Matrah, near Muscat, with the hope of buying land and erecting a hospital in the near future. Early in 1910, also, Kuweit, important as the key to the interior of the Nejd, was reopened by medical workers from Busrah, and later in the year land was obtained on which to erect a hospital and other mission buildings.

Vignettes. At Kuweit, Mrs. E. E. Calverly, M.D., now in charge of the hospital and dispensary work, comes daily in contact with the sorrows and sufferings of Arab women. From her sketch in *Medical Missions*, February, 1916, omitting quotation marks, we give the following vivid pictures, as typical of the intercourse between our missionary physicians and Moslem women in all lands.

Come with me for a little visit to Arabia, our adopted country. It will mean a sea voyage of six or seven weeks to reach our home in Kuweit. We must cross the Atlantic, skirt the southern coast of Europe, pass through the Suez Canal, through the Red Sea, along the southern coast of the Arabian peninsula to Bombay, and from there take another ship and steam northward up the Persian Gulf, along the eastern coast of Arabia, to Kuweit.

Home life of the women. Arab houses are built around a central court, a square of ground exposed to the sky, and having all the windows and doors of the surrounding rooms open into it. There are no outside windows lest passers-by should catch a glimpse of the women of the household. Some of the highest class of women do not go outside the four walls of their house from the time they are brought as brides of twelve or thirteen years to the home of the husband, until they are carried out to the graveyard. The middle class have more freedom, but they must never go out unless their faces are entirely covered with the black veil and cloak,—leaving just as little an opening in the cloak as is really necessary in order to see the road.

The wealthy houses have a second courtyard exclusively for the women, and which can be reached only by passing through the men's court. A man will not trust his father or his brother to see the face of his wife. Even the poor Bedouin Arabs, who spend their lives wandering over the desert from oasis to oasis, have their tents divided by a curtain through the centre so that the men may sit on one side and the women on the other.

At meal time the dinner is brought to the heads of the house, and not until after these have ceased to eat do the women sit down to eat what is left. A man would not condescend to eat with a woman. I knew an old man who loved his daughter dearly and used to call her to sit by his side while he ate, but she might not eat with him because he was a man and she was a woman!

A man will not condescend to walk with his wife on the street. If they must walk to the same place, he walks ahead and she behind; and if there is a burden to carry, it is the wife who bears it on her head.

Social life of Arab women. As soon as we moved into our little house in Kuweit, Arab visitors began to come. By twos and threes the women entered our courtyard, black shrouded figures. They were welcomed and conducted to the room which serves as church on Sunday, schoolroom on weekdays, and reception-room after school hours. Here I could assure them that they could remove their veils without fear of having their faces seen by any man.

A Sunday school picture roll hung on the wall, and this seldom failed to excite questions and give us a chance to tell the Bible stories which they represented. Then there was a baby organ. The women had never seen an organ before, and always wanted us to play and sing to them. This furnished us an opportunity to explain such hymns as "Jesus loves me," and "I need Thee every hour."

An Arab lady of Persia. One day the wife of a very wealthy Arab came to see me. She was very haughty and reticent at first, as she sat there dressed in her silks and jewels, but after we had done our best to entertain her, and served refreshments in Arab style, she began to tell her troubles.

"You know," she said, "Khatoon, my husband has another wife. I have never seen her. She lives in another house, and just as I have two children—so has she. She hates me and I hate her. My husband says he cannot afford to keep two houses; that we must live together. I can't do it! I won't do it! I will die first!"

* * * * * * *

Relieving the suffering. The medical work allows one to get an even more intimate knowledge of the life of the Arab woman. When we went to Kuweit the people had never before seen a woman missionary, and most of them had never seen any other white woman.

Two rooms of a native house built of mud and plaster, a big table, a little table, a chair and a bench, a box, and some basins for washing the hands; these, and a pink calico curtain, stretched across one of the rooms used for examination and treatment, constituted the equipment of the Woman's Hospital of Kuweit in the beginning. At first there were few patients and much distrust. During the last year we were frequently asked to treat members of the royal household, who contributed generously to the support of the hospital. My Arab costume was a gift from the wife of the heir-apparent to the throne.

If we had been doubtful as to whether medical work was having any effect upon Kuweit, we were reassured when the prominent Arabs of the town held a meeting and decided to send for a Turkish doctor and establish a Moslem dispensary where the poor might be treated free without coming under Christian influence. The doctor came and spent much money on equipment, but his work was not very successful and he was not willing to treat the poor free, because he had not the spirit of Christ as an incentive. In a few months he became so unpopular that he left town, leaving all his drugs to be confiscated by the ruling sheik.

At first the patients were sometimes afraid to take our medicine, but confidence grew. Toward the end of our stay in Arabia I was called to see a woman whom I had never met before. She was suffering terribly, but I feared she would not allow an operation which was necessary. Before I had even time to suggest an operation, she said: "Doctor, do with me as you think best. I have perfect confidence in you. You may even cut me open if you like." How sad it would have been had this woman's confidence been in vain. God blessed the operation and she recovered, and became our firm friend.

Our opponents also threatened to secure a Moslem woman-doctor to be my rival; but we were not greatly alarmed at this talk, for we knew that in the whole Turkish Empire there was but one woman with a license to practise medicine, and she was a Christian missionary.

The work was not always encouraging; but one day we chanced to overhear a conversation between two women patients.

"The doctor," said one, "takes just as much pains with those who cannot pay as with the rich patients."

"Yes," said the other, "and look at her dressing that dirty ulcer on that poor woman. What Moslem would do that?"

We have prayed that they might see from our lives that the religion of Jesus Christ gives something which they need, and do not have.

Six days a week the waiting-room of the women's dispensary is more or less filled with women and children of every station in life and all degrees of intelligence. When the crowd seems to have reached its largest size—twenty, thirty, or even forty patients, besides their companions who do not come for treatment—all treatments are stopped for about ten minutes while the doctor takes her seat with the patients gathered before her on the floor or bench. There is sometimes great confusion, with the women laughing and talking and babies crying. It takes several minutes to get them all quiet. "Do not talk," we say in Arabic. "Keep quiet," the assistant says in Persian, "you women over there in the corner; the doctor's going to pray and ask God to heal your diseases."

Finally, when all is quiet, we begin by a short prayer asking God's blessing on each one, and especially upon the reading which is to follow. The prayer is very simple, but God has many times answered our request.

3. Turkey and Syria

"Thus saith the Lord God, Remove the diadem, and take off the crown; this shall not be the same; exalt him that is low and abase him that is high. I will overturn, overturn, overturn it; and it shall be no more, until He come whose right it is, and I will give it him."

Prophecy of Ezekiel.

The world war has changed the face of Christian missions in the Turkish Empire. In this, one of the earliest of our foreign fields, we find today the name of one station after another in our annual reports followed by a blank, by the words, "to await the outcome of the war," or with names of one or two lonely missionaries who remain behind of their own choice at imminent peril.

With the Armenian nation scattered and all but exterminated, missions among them are of necessity

at a standstill. Nowhere have conditions been more
thrillingly set forth than in the book, *An American
Physician in Turkey*, by Dr. C. D. Ussher, an incom-
parable record of heroism without heroics. What
was true of the mission in Van,—complete destruction,—has been true in general throughout Turkish
missions.

The new day. All things being in transition no
element now remains stable but
hope; hope, however, has grown, of a sudden, to
startling proportions. Under after-war conditions,
with the breaking-up of the Turkish Empire, with
the establishment of an autonomous Armenia, and,
it may be, a Christian-controlled Palestine all in
sight, a new and glorious era for Christian Missions
is clearly at hand. The Pride of Islam is crumbling,
the soldiers of the Crescent henceforth will present
a less fierce and inflexible resistance to the soldiers
of the Cross. We may look for mighty changes and
speedy ones.

It is not, then, the moment for survey of Christian
Missions in these lands in the past, nor even in the
present. It is the hour of the future, the hour of
expectation.

Firm Nevertheless, it is an hour for pro-
Foundations. found thanksgiving that in the century just closing, the century which began in November, 1819, with the mission to Palestine of Pliny
Fiske and Levi Parsons, foundations broad and deep
have been laid in these strongholds of Mohammedanism for the superstructure which may soon arise to
gladden Christendom. The personnel of the American Mission to Turkey, from the beginning, has been

peculiarly adequate and distinguished by eminent attainment in all branches of missionary service, whether evangelistic, educational, or medical. The latter has, from the first, been accorded prominence. Just before the opening of the war the situation of medical work was thus given in brief: "The American Board has nine hospitals in Turkey, all in the interior of the Asiatic portion. Almost all of them maintain dispensaries and outside practice, as well as conduct the distinctive work of a hospital. In these nine institutions last year there were treated three thousand, four hundred and one in-patients, while to the dispensaries came twenty-eight thousand, nine hundred and thirty-four patients who received one hundred and twelve thousand, eight hundred and thirty treatments. Each of these hospitals serves a wide area, patients coming from hundreds of towns and villages." These hospitals were located at Marsovan, Cesarea, Sivas, Aintab, Harput, Van, Mardin, Erzroom, and Diarbekir and to them is added the International Hospital at Adana and the American Christian Hospital at Konia, Asia Minor.

Christian unity realized. Dr. Ussher of Van says, "Although our Board is a Congregational Board, fifty-eight per cent. of its missionaries represent a number of other denominations; in the Eastern Turkey Mission there were Congregationalists, Presbyterians, Methodists, Baptists, Disciples, Episcopalians, and Lutherans, all working together in perfect harmony, and with no reference to differences in creed or ritual."

This suggestive summary may be supplemented

by allusion to the unfailing provision for the treatment of women and children and to the heroic labors of women as physicians, nurses, and hospital superintendents in the work in Turkey. Dr. Caroline Hamilton at Aintab, Dr. Ida Stapleton at Erzroom, and Dr. Ruth Parmelee at Harput have won their way as qualified physicians and have contributed not a little towards changing the Moslem conceptions of woman's place in the scale of being. The Christian hospitals are, with probably no exception, equipped with wards or special buildings for women and children, while the dispensaries have been carefully arranged, so that the Moslem women may receive treatment without incurring the danger of being seen of men.

War's wreck. It is an interesting fact that at six mission stations in Turkey women and only women are remaining; at the rest one or two men "hold the fort." Everywhere the devastation of war has broken up the work and scattered the workers. As typical of present conditions we call attention to the report for 1917 of the mission station at Harput on the Euphrates River amid the foothills of the Taurus mountains. This station, widely known and well since 1855, had on its list of active service at the outbreak of the war fourteen ordained pastors, twenty-one ordained preachers, and one hundred teachers, men and women. At present, so far as is known, one pastor survives, three unordained preachers in Harput and three in exile are living, and twenty teachers remain. All of the forty-three schools are closed and the buildings

either destroyed or in the hands of the Turks. Of
the thirty-six churches all are gone save one, the
church in Harput proper. Euphrates College was
closed in February, 1915, its professors were arrested,
subjected to terrible treatment and to tortures so
extreme that in most cases death followed. The
Euphrates Medical Association conducted, in affilia-
tion with the college and hospital, a class in midwifery. A nurses' training school, a dispensary and
infirmary for orphan children were also carried on.
This hospital, begun by Dr. H. H. Atkinson with
the co-operation of his wife in 1902 in a single room,
with an outfit costing two hundred dollars, has now
become the Annie Tracey Riggs Memorial Hospital,
a finely equipped building on a beautiful site a few
miles out of Harput. But all is now changed, albeit
the hospital has been open without interruption
since the beginning of the war for sick and wounded
soldiers who were cared for in large part by Christian
attendants and under Christian influence. No one
can estimate the value of the seed thus sown in
the hearts of many Moslem soldiers. Dr. Atkinson
died of typhus in December, 1915. When the missionaries left Harput in May, 1917, the hospital
was left in the hands of the military authorities. At
the personal request of Mrs. Atkinson, however,
the part of the hospital that had been used for poor
Christian patients was still kept for that purpose,
and the income from the sale of the hospital drugs
was, at last accounts, being used to support a con-
siderable number of Christian patients in that
hospital, under the care of military doctors.

The return of the Turkey missionaries. It is with profound satisfaction that as this book goes to press the American Board gives the information following: Turkey agreed to capitulate on Thursday, October 31. The articles of capitulation and armistice were signed on the Island of Lemnos, Friday, November 1. On Wednesday, October 30, in anticipation of these events, the Foreign Secretary of the Board, Dr. James L. Barton, in company with Mr. W. W. Peet, the treasurer of our missions in the Near East, waited upon Secretary Lansing and other government officials at Washington and obtained consent for our Turkey missionaries to return at the earliest date when sailing arrangements can be made. Dr. James L. Barton and President E. C. Moore of the Board headed a Commission which started for the Near East January first, 1919. No time must be lost in rendering relief to the stricken populations, both Christian and Moslem. Fully half of the Armenian race in the Ottoman Empire has perished, and over two million Moslems have died through famine and disease, brought upon them by their own mad rulers. Those who remain are in dire distress.

The Commission of seven, starting in advance, will be followed by the larger body of relief workers. This group will include the greater majority of American Board and Presbyterian missionaries to Turkey, who have been detained in this country or forced to return here by the war. They will go, many of them, to stations where they were before attached; will deal with regions and races with which they are familiar; and will be able to render immediate service, because of their knowledge of language and custom, their personal acquaintance with the people, Turks as well as others, and the confidence which they have won in the labors of former years. By their coming they will enable the fifty or more American Board missionaries who have remained in Turkey during these terrible years to get away for the furloughs that are long overdue.

The relief body will include a medical unit, headed by Dr. Washburn, of Boston. It will include surgeons, specialists and general practitioners, nurses and hospital orderlies. Supplies of hospital furnishings, medicines, etc., are being collected. This party hopes to sail early in January.

Syria. In 1870, the Board of Foreign Missions of the Presbyterian Church in the U. S. A., North, took over the work in Syria and has conducted it with characteristic organizing ability. Medical work here, as everywhere else, was carried on, able physicians from the first entering the field. The famous translator of the Bible, Dr. Van Dyck, equally distinguished as scholar and physician, was one of the first of these. Regular medical mission stations were established with centres at Beirut and Tripoli. All the spiritual and intellectual life which ennobles Syria has had its source in Beirut, seat of the Syrian Protestant College.

The medical work in Syria in the past has been furthered by the presence in Beirut of the Johanniter Hospital, with its spacious buildings and fine facilities. The management of this hospital well illustrates co-operation in benevolence. The property is owned and the hospital maintained by the Johanniter Order, popularly known as the Knights of St. John. The nurses are provided by the deaconesses of Kaiserswerth, and the medical and surgical staff by the Syrian Protestant College at Beirut. The medical department of the College gives a thorough four years' course. The effect of this is seen in the steadily advancing standard of medical training throughout Syria.

The Maria de Witt Jessup Hospitals for women and children were opened in 1905, in a temporary home. In the autumn of 1907, a new women's pavilion was completed; an eye and ear pavilion has been added and a hospital for children with forty-five beds. A nurses' training school for Syrian girls is under the direction of American nurses. Mrs. Gerald F. Dale, in 1905, became the superintendent of these hospitals. Mrs. Dale says:

"We can accommodate one hundred and thirty patients. They come from all parts of Syria and Palestine, from Egypt, Cyprus, Constantinople, Russia, and various parts of Asia Minor. They range from the Persian lady of wealth, to the goatherd, who tossed about in misery, because the pillow was too soft, the bed too easy, and he longed to lie down on mother earth, with nothing but the sky above him!"

The work of Dr. Mary P. Eddy is also associated with Beirut station. On returning to her native Syria in 1893, after a complete medical course in the United States, Dr. Eddy succeeded by long patience in obtaining the degree of doctor of medicine and surgery from the Turkish Government, with permission to practice anywhere in the Empire. This was the first government

HACKETT MEDICAL COLLEGE, CANTON, CHINA

Students Playing Basketball

(By permission of the Foreign Missions Library)

degree ever given to a woman. For some years Dr. Eddy spent most of her time in medical and evangelistic tours through the entire mission field, in the service of women particularly.

In 1903, Dr. Eddy opened a hospital and dispensary for women at Junieh, fifteen miles across the bay from Beirut. The medical work is firmly established; there are regular Sabbath services; schools for the boys and girls; a Bible Society colporteur working in the villages; a Bible woman to visit in the neighborhood and among the patients. On the hospital premises are a resting room, a guest chamber for missionaries, a reading room and a Bible depository. Regular clinics are held for Moslem women. Many Kurds and Bedouins also attend. These wanderers have learned to trust Dr. Eddy, and when their tents are invaded by illness they take refuge in her vicinity.

Tubercular disease, both medical and surgical, is extremely prevalent in Syria. The people have an unreasoning dread of it, and the sufferers are often driven out from their homes and left to perish without care or comfort. One woman, discharged from a non-Christian hospital, walked the streets of Beirut for hours, seeking a resting place. No one would listen to her, and when night fell she took refuge under the arches of a bridge, with a stone for her pillow, and lay there for five days. Some passers-by were finally moved to build a little hut for her, but the terrified neighbors threatened nightly to come and burn both it and her. Dr. Eddy heard of her need, and at once took her in and cared lovingly for her until her death.

Moved by this and other distressing cases, Dr. Eddy opened, in 1908, a small sanitarium for tuberculous patients. By the gifts of the women of Washington (D. C.) Presbytery, the Hamlin Memorial Hospital was built at Maamaltain, on Junieh Bay, and also a summer camp at Shebaniyeh, about four thousand feet up, on a spur of the Lebanon mountains. Here the patients are housed in separate shelters, given by Dr. Eddy's friends in commemoration of the twentieth year of her service in Syria. About fifty patients can be cared for, and pitiful appeals from much larger numbers are continually received. This is the only institution of the kind in all the Turkish Empire.

The Tripoli Hospital has forty beds, and for six

years, 1908 to 1914, had on its staff a woman physician, Dr. Elsie Harris, daughter of the physician
in charge. Religious services are held in the hospital
chapel. Dispensaries are conducted at Hums and
Hamath.

Syrian missions have suffered severely from the
strain and stress of war, in particular from the
prevalence of typhus fever, which has spread like a
conflagration over the Turkish Empire, from conditions among the armies of soldiers as among the
armies of refugees. A native survivor out of great
tribulation declares that there are hardly ten thousand men left in the city of Beirut and that in
brief time hunger, disease, and the atrocity of the
Turk will leave practically no men in the city. This
man adds, "I am now under the English rule in
Jerusalem and am very happy that I have got free
from the Turkish yoke."

The Holy Land. The whole Christian world rejoices
in the release of the city of David
and of great David's greater Son from the abomina-
ble grasp of the Turk. Brief time has elapsed since
General Allenby with his troops entered Jerusalem,
and went on his conquering course through the
Holy Land, but already we hear of the new day
which has dawned upon the people who sat in darkness and in the shadow of death, bound with afflic-
tion and iron. Everywhere can be seen signs of
reviving courage, initiative, and energy. Peace,
security, industrial prosperity are manifest even now.
The people hail the new era opening for their land.

Who can doubt that, as the Sun of Righteousness
arises with healing in His wings over this sacred

soil, so long despoiled and desecrated, the Church in America will know a revival of missionary zeal? Shall we not look to see the movement of a new crusade of compassion for the oppressed daughters of Jerusalem?

Hitherto our American Mission Boards have gained little permanent footing in Palestine. The Kaiserswerth Deaconesses organization, founded in Syria in 1851 by a German missionary, the Rev. T. H. Fliedner, instituted important work in nursing the sick in the city of Jerusalem; this sisterhood, until the war, had carried on a sanatorium on the Heights of Godfrey, northwest of the city. Orphanages under various auspices exist at different points throughout Syria. A new one, to meet war conditions, has recently been opened at Jaffa by the agent of the British and Foreign Bible Society.

Extensive medical mission work in Palestine, prior to the war, was conducted under the following Societies:

The Church Missionary Society, Salisbury Square, London, England, with hospitals in Gaza, Jaffa, Nablus, and Es-Salt.

London Jews Society, 16 Lincoln's Inn Fields, W. C., with large Jewish hospital at Jerusalem.

The Edinburgh Medical Mission, with hospitals at Nazareth, Tiberias, and Safed.

Jerusalem and the East Mission, under the Anglican Bishop in Jerusalem, with St. Helena's Medical Mission and Nursing Home at Jerusalem, and a hospital at Haifa.

4. Egypt

In the old, familiar story of Joseph we read of a
company of Ishmaelites coming from Gilead beyond
Jordan, with their camels, bearing spicery and balm
and myrrh, going to carry it down to Egypt. It was
a journey frequently and quickly made, and it is
the one we now make, without the aid of camels,
from the Land of ancient Promise to the Land of
ancient Bondage.

Egypt is the threshold by which we enter Africa
from the East, rather than an integral part of Africa
itself. Its general features resemble those of Syria
and Arabia. (In Lower Egypt the Moslems form
about ninety-eight per cent. of the population, and
in Upper Egypt about eighty-eight per cent.). The
Copts, a decadent survival racially of the ancient
Egyptians and religiously of the early Christian
Church planted in Alexandria by the Apostles, constitute less than seven hundred thousand in a population of over eleven million. The stay and backbone
of the Coptic nationality is its church, under a
Patriarch to whom all classes render reverence.
Superstition, ignorance and avarice have indeed eat-
en out the life of this once truly Christian society;
none the less the Copts are far more accessible
to the Gospel than are the Moslems.

English and American influence.   The British occupation, begun in
1882, when anarchy reigned supreme
under Moslem mismanagement, has
produced a new Egypt and a vastly better one, in
which progress, industrial, moral and social, has
been astonishing. English rule has brought in its

train a revival of English missions. The orderly extension of the work of the C. M. S. (Church Missionary Society) dates, however, only from 1898, when a mission hospital was built in Old Cairo and extensive work inaugurated.

Antedating the C. M. S.* by over thirty years is the remarkable mission carried on by the United Presbyterians of the United States, known better as the American Mission, in large-minded indifference to sectarian considerations. The Church which this mission has built up is known throughout the Nile Valley as "the Protestant Church" or "the Evangelical Church." It was founded in Cairo in 1854 by Rev. Thomas McCague and in 1869 the church numbered one hundred and eighty members. There were stations in several places, the strongest centre being at Assiut; in 1895 the number of communicants had risen to four thousand, five hundred and fifty-four. Work was carried on among Moslems as well as Copts, although progress is slow, indeed, among the former, and little wonder, since it is true that the Mohammedan would rather kill his brother, his father, or his son with his own hand than see him turn Christian.

In 1890, a forward movement began in the American Mission, one result of which was the extension of the work to several towns in the Nile Delta, notably Tanta, the Mecca of Egypt; another being the strengthening of the medical work, heretofore merely incidental. In 1901 a large hospital was built in

---

* See *The King's Highway*, H. B. Montgomery, page 13 ff. Central Committee on the United Study of Foreign Missions, 1915.

Assiut, and in 1902 two medical women missionaries
began their work in Tanta. A comfortable hospital
for women and children is now established in the
latter city and the work has extended to Luxor,
Benha, and Fayum, with several physicians, both
men and women, in charge and a fairly adequate
nursing staff. Forty thousand people annually are
treated by the medical missionaries, but the crying
need of Egypt remains more hospitals for women
and children, more Christian women to take up
medical work among them. The Church reaches the
poor of the cities and the peasants of outlying villages
mainly through the daily clinic, as in other countries
which have come under our observation. Dr. Caroline C. Lawrence of the Tanta Hospital describes
a typical scene in the Egyptian dispensary when the
Bible woman gathers the people about her, while
they await the presence of the physician, and reads
the Bible stories and parables, and transposes them
into homely, every-day Arabic. "One day," writes
Dr. Lawrence, "a graphic description is given of the
wonderful clinics held by the Great Physician with
a leading-up to the need of healing sin-sick souls.
Again it is the parables. Thus patiently the story
which we have to tell them is unfolded. The audience
shows its appreciation by responses of approval and
surprise. With the audience there is no question of
creed or interpretation. It is the painstaking, oft-
repeated instillation of the essential doctrines: the
reality of sinfulness, the need of repentance, salvation
through Christ."

Mention must be made of the College for young
women at Cairo, from among whose students we

may look in time for native physicians. Its impress is plainly perceptible in the social and home life of the better class of Egyptians. It has, indeed, been called "the greatest asset for the introduction and dissemination of Christian ideals and influence in Egypt."

We have a continent before us and cannot tarry longer on its threshold, but, as we leave Egypt, we leave behind, westward, facing Europe, between the Mediterranean and the Great Desert, Tripoli, Tunis, Algeria, Morocco, strongholds of Mohammedanism, lurking-places of darkness and iniquity indescribable. Here is one of the danger spots of the globe, one of the fields which call loudest for the invasion in force of the Battalion of Life.

Note: For general reading we recommend "American Healing around the World," by Edgar Allen Forbes in December World's Work, 1907.

MARGARET WILLIAMSON HOSPITAL, SHANGHAI, CHINA

(By permission of the Woman's Union Missionary Society)

CHAPTER VI.

AFRICA AND THE PROMISE OF THE FUTURE

"I wish to testify to what seemed to me the enormously important work that is being done by missionaries. . . . In the Congo almost the only people who are working in behalf of the natives are those attached to the missions. . . . It is due to them that Europe and the United States know the truth about the Congo. They were the first to bear witness, and the hazardous work they still are doing for their fellowmen is honest, practical Christianity."

Richard Harding Davis.

AFRICA

IT is impossible to open even a superficial study of Africa without meeting the fact of the mighty advance which Islam has made within less than a score of years, of its present prevailing influence not only on the fringe of the vast continent, but in the interior. Says Dr. Patton, "Until the facts were made known at the Edinburgh Conference (1910), Christian people had no idea of this new Mohammedan peril. They are beginning now to realize that all Central Africa is threatened, that this is not a matter of the neglect of the Church five hundred years ago, but of the neglect of the Church today. Surely, we must move quickly if we are to save the situation in Central Africa." The testimony of Mohammedan aggression comes from the East coast and the West, and even from Liberia.

As a symptom of the oncoming tide of Mohammedanism we are told of a high priest of that religion who visited Monrovia, the capital of the Republic of Liberia, last July. Coming from the French Sudan, his arrival was heralded long in advance. His journey through the bush was nothing less than a triumphal procession. He came to Monrovia to gain permission to establish Mohammedan mosques and schools throughout the Republic. For a couple of weeks he remained moving about with a large company of his followers who sang as they marched through the streets. Special attendants carried his umbrella, his chair, and supported his staff. This assumption of royal state notably appealed to the native man's fancy and the influence gained by this priest among them seems boundless.

The Methodist Episcopal Mission at Inhambane gives striking confirmation of the foregoing, as follows:

Ever aggressive, alert, subtle, and adopting up-to-date methods for reaching the people, such as the singing of songs and the training of women and girls in its schools, Mohammedanism is making renewed and strenuous efforts to win Inhambane for the false prophet. The spirit of Islam is the same today as when the followers of Mahomet made its converts with the sword. Just at this moment they dare not adopt that method here, but they use every other method at their disposal to make converts. Intermarriage plays a very important part in their campaign. More and larger Mohammedan settlements are scattered throughout the country and each community is a camp of aggressive Moslem propaganda. The red fez and the white flowing robes are seen in larger numbers today than ever before. May the following be indelibly stamped upon our hearts: Ten thousand young Moslems are in training in Cairo as missionaries of the Crescent to Africa. The fight is on. It will be a fight to a finish. It is made more difficult because of the subtle methods adopted by this power. Using a military term, "sniping" is practiced in a very large measure by its followers.

The hope of the present hour is that the Church will awake to the danger and act in the crisis of a probable disintegration among the Moslem forces created by the defeat of Turkey in the Great War. The solidarity of Islam has been shaken. It is the time for holy strategy and commanding Christian statesmanship.

Nearly one-fourth of all the land surface of the earth is in the continent of Africa, i.e., twelve million square miles.

The distance around the coast of Africa is as great as that around the world.

Eight hundred and forty-two languages and dialects are in use among the black people of Africa.

One out of every ten of the inhabitants of Africa is a Moslem.

There is one missionary for every one hundred and thirty-six thousand souls and an area unoccupied by missionaries which equals three times New England plus four times New York plus eight times Iowa plus eighteen times Ohio.

Animism and Fetishism constitute the religion of the natives, a form of paganism which fills the whole universe and all material objects with spirits, usually evil—a most brutal and degrading religion. Pagans number eighty million; Mohammedans, forty million; Christians, ten million.

Since African missions and African pagan peoples have been recently the subject of united study, it may fairly be inferred that general conditions, and facts concerning the degradation of women are now familiar. Space will be given, therefore, to medical work only, and in particular to the medical work of women missionaries.

The world's Short and simple, indeed, are the
open sore. annals over which we bend. In all this vast continent are to be found under missionary auspices eighty-five hospitals; about one hundred men physicians and fifteen women physicians. The hopeful question springs to mind, among a hardy, primitive people, not enervated by civilization, is it not true that generally healthy conditions prevail, rendering the practice of surgery and medicine in large degree superfluous?

If we could but lay such flattering unction to our souls to soothe the sharp compunction of our Christian conscience! Unhappily, we cannot. The question meets an unqualified *No*. The wastage of human life in Africa and the needless torturing of it are terrible to contemplate. As we read of conditions of life in this outer darkness of paganism the words of the prophet Isaiah alone suffice for description:

> The whole head is sick, and the whole heart faint.
> From the sole of the foot even unto the head there is no soundness in it;
> But wounds and bruises, and putrefying sores:
> They have not been closed, neither bound up, neither mollified with ointment.

In very truth, festering wounds caused by mutilation for mysterious purposes of adornment are to be seen on all sides. Smallpox, epilepsy, and rheumatism prevail widely.

African diseases. Besides these, the sleeping sickness is the cause of terrible loss of life. Hemorrhagic and other deadly fevers, dysentery, anaemia, hook worm disease, ophthalmia, pterygium, leprosy, indolent ulcers, tumors of enormous size, malformations, intestinal parasites, filaria loa (which travels under the eye ball under the conjunctiva), malaria, typhus and typhoid, helpless and hopeless insanity, cause measureless suffering. The need for medical men and women can scarcely be overestimated. Even toothache has its torments.

The need for the Battalion of Life in Africa is nowhere more clearly shown than in the condition of the mothers and the children. We find that when the stork comes the mother is treated with great cruelty. It is tabu for her to eat or drink anything, and she is told that it would kill the child if she does. Should the birth be difficult, divinatory bones are consulted and the woman may be removed to another place. If the birth is delayed, the midwife thereby knows that the child is illegitimate, and confession is extorted by divination. Pumpkin seeds are put into a broken pot and placed on the fire. If the seeds explode, instead of burning to a cinder, that is proof that the woman is guilty. Each explosion means a lover, and all the names must be revealed before the delaying hindrance can be removed. The husband is not allowed to approach the hut, as he would undergo pollution if he did so. The floor of the hut is cleansed by the mother of the woman, who smears it with clay to purify it. The lack of cleanliness on the occasion of childbirth is the cause of an appalling loss of human life.

Besides the witchcraft and magic and charms, which are said to be responsible for more wastage of human life even than slavery, another source of wastage is the appallingly wholesale administration of native drugs. Hundreds of lives are lost through the ignorance, superstition, and malignity of such treatments. A picture of the poisoner at work even in the wards of the hospital, surreptitiously trying to destroy many lives, and of the incendiary without any pretext firing a house and burning all in it might be seen, if we could but lift the fringe of the curtain that veils heathendom.

The witch doctor.   Much of the physical suffering in Africa is due to the horrible practices of the witch doctor, the all-powerful authority for mind and body to the superstitious native. "He is a great foe to the missionary, a bitter opponent to the Gospel. He tells the people that the missionary comes to buy their souls and take them away to the foreign country to re-embody them as slaves. This and other falsehoods he makes the people believe, that he may hinder them from embracing the teachings of the missionary, and from accepting the Gospel of Christ. Like the silversmiths of Ephesus, he knows that his craft is in danger, and he must hold his power over the people to secure his gains."

How is the witch doctor prepared for his work? The dogma that rules his practice is that in all cases of disease in which no blood is showing the patient is suffering from something wrong in one of his many souls. Trouble at night means that the *dream-soul* is disturbed. He is thought to possess a witch power and the knowledge of how to employ it, and this

secures for him esteem and honor; the more terrific
this power is known to be the more respect he gains.
In every village there are secret societies for men
and for women. The elders discover a person, man
or woman, who has power to see spirits. Such are
advised to be apprenticed to a witch doctor, who
requires a good fee for the training. He learns the
difference between the dream-soul basket and the
one others are kept in, and a mistake would be on a
par with mistaking oxalic acid for epsom salts. He
is then taught how to howl professionally, and, by
watching his professor, he picks up his bedside
mannerisms. He must also learn how to make charms
to protect his patients and their wives and children,
their goats, plantations, canoes, etc. He must also
be skilled in detecting the guilty odor of crime.

Charms and   It is said that all the ocean liners
amulets.   which cross the deep would not more
than contain the amulets, charms, trinkets, fetish-
es, and the whole vast paraphernalia of heathenism
which has found its genesis in superstition. A spec-
tral world of demons, dragons, goblins, imps, thronging spirits of evil, seems to fill the haunted imagination of otherwise sane and sober people given over
to what Sir Monier-Williams designates as "demon-
ophobia." In the clear and innocent look of a friend
there is cause to fear the evil eye,—while foreboding
terror and the dismal follies of witchcraft play havoc
at a moment's notice with social order and with
every principle of piety and justice. Physical ills
such as sickness, pain, or calamity are traced to the
anger of some unseen evil spirit, malevolent fiend,
or dragon visitor in the night. At whatever cost

some method of propitiation must be devised to ward off the disaster. Even some innocent neighbor or dead relative may be suspected of fiendish machinations and then that principal of all quacks and deceivers, "the smelling-out doctor," must be called to localize the source of the trouble and advise some method of dealing with it.

Superstitions like these are formidable, but not impassable barriers to the Gospel of Christ. Harnack says:

"Jesus Christ was the first to bring the value of every human soul to light, and what He did no one can undo. Since His day those with the highest ideals always reverence personality, and hold inviolate the sanctity of womanhood and of the inner nature. Failure at this point is not failure at the circumference but at the center. A low and enfeebled conception of God results in a depreciated estimate of personality. This is true of paganism. Christ discovered the individual. It is the office of medical missions to interpret this discovery in pagan lands."

Houses changed to homes.   The effect of this interpretation is seen in houses changed to homes. The missionary's house becomes the home for the friendless, an orphanage for the fatherless, a refuge for the oppressed, a school for the ignorant, a workshop for the unemployed, a lawyer's office for the perplexed, a hospital for the sick, a resting-place for the stranger, and a Bethel for weary souls. The changing of houses into homes was a thing unknown in Africa before the introduction of Christianity. Flowers appear in the homes of those who, before their conversion, never saw their beauty or understood the ministry of those silent witnesses. There is a marked improvement in the order and cleanliness of the rooms, indicative of a growing desire to live out religion. There is a deepening conviction in the hearts of those who feel the call of God to preach the Gospel, that the ministry is the noblest work in which they can engage, and many refuse employment which offers much higher remuneration. In token of generosity, giving amounts to $7.50 per capita, per annum; in the measure of Christian character, missionary zeal, and sacrificial giving the African convert measures up to the standard.

Livingstone's legacy.   Despite superstition, savagery and degradation we have Livingstone's word that "Heathen Africans are much superior to the Mohammedans, who are the most worthless one can have." Among these people in Southern and Central Africa Dr. Livingstone labored mightily, "preaching the Gospel and healing diseases" from 1841 to 1856. When he severed his connection with the London Missionary Society in order to enter upon explorations whereby to combat the slave-trade, he declared, "The opening of the new central country is a matter for congratulation only so far as it opens up a prospect for the elevation of the inhabitants. I go back to Africa to make an open path for commerce and Christianity. I view the geographical exploration as the beginning of the missionary enterprise. I include in the latter term everything in the way of effort for the amelioration of our race." It need scarcely be said that in this purpose the treatment of disease and the alleviation of suffering must have held a high place.

It would be impossible within the limits of this chapter to enumerate the many missions which have been initiated for the natives of Africa in the century since Robert Moffat (in 1816), began his work in Bechuana Land. Many of these were short-lived; in many cases work was transferred from its original *locale* to another more promising. It is true that all African missions received a strong incentive from the initiative of Livingstone and from the solemn legacy of those words of his, spoken in England in 1857, "Do you carry out the work which I have begun; I leave it with you." The opening of the Congo State in 1884 furnished a second challenge to the spirit of Missions to which quick response was made; at this time the Livingstone Inland Mission was transferred to American Baptists. All our major American denominational Boards, thirty-six in all, now sustain missions in Africa, but, while in nearly all a certain amount of medical service is rendered through dispensary practice, we do not find this branch as thoroughly organized, manned, and equipped as in Asiatic missions, despite the great demand. Africa is obviously the most difficult field for which to provide missionary physicians, especially women physicians.

A few glimpses of routine work will enable us to estimate in some small degree the trials and the rewards which attend the service of those who brave the dangers of climate and uncivilization and enter here upon the crusade of compassion.

Apostles of peace. The Society of Friends in 1902 established a mission in the Kavirondo country, British East Africa. A hospital has been

erected at Kaimosi, and is now under the management of Dr. A. A. Bond and Mrs. Bond. We quote
from their letters:

April 15, 1917. Dr. Bond has fixed up one room for a dispensary and has already had quite a practice. It will take time
to get the natives to be willing to come and stay here while
they are sick, but they will come to it gradually. They are so
bound by their old superstitions and customs, especially the
old people. The young people are much more easily persuaded
to take medicine. Several have already been here. They have
lots of sores and ulcers. It is pitiful to see the little babies with
these skin diseases. Some babies have been brought who have
burns. The mothers have to go away to work in their gardens
and while they are gone the babies, who are left at home on
the floor, roll into the fire which is in the middle of the hut
floor.

May 7, 1917. During the first month I treated about one
hundred and fifty dispensary patients, made five trips into the
reserve, gave medical attention to six missionaries and other
whites and made one trip eighty miles distant to see a sick
settler. During the second month I treated seven hundred and
fifty dispensary patients, made fifteen visits into the reserve
and gave medical attention to ten missionaries and other whites.
There is certainly a great field for medical work here and I
believe that it will contribute much to the missionary work as
soon as we get the hospital started, as it will give an additional
point of contact with the natives and help to win their confidence.

July 1, 1917. The medical work continues to increase and
the outlook is very promising in this connection. The suffering
due to ignorance, superstition, and filthy living is almost unbelievable.

The not-afraid   The results following the work of the
religion.   medical missionary are sometimes
encouraging and sometimes tax one's patience and
faith. Occasionally, however, a testimony like the

following comes which makes the worker realize that no other department of the Mission appeals to the West African as does the medical work. He cannot read well, if at all. He does not always understand the preacher, but he does seem to comprehend the love of God when he sees it illustrated by the tender ministry that seeks to relieve his suffering.

"A woman afflicted with a malignant ulcer had lain several years on her bed without improvement. Her friends brought her, saying,—'This woman is dead unless you can cure her.' After three months in the hospital, she was discharged, cured, and best of all she had *learned to know her Saviour*. She went back to her town at some distance and held meetings for the women to tell them what she had learned of Jesus. Occasionally she would come back to the station saying, 'I have told them all I know; tell me more that I may repeat it to them.' She was given Sunday School pictures with the requisite explanations and these she would carry back to her class. One day she returned with twenty women, who she said wanted to know more about 'the Gospel that makes people not afraid of evil spirits.'"

A brave woman.   "Medical work is still of the most primitive kind in Liberia. No white physician has ventured there, but Miss Sarah E. Conway, a trained nurse, is in charge of a clinic, run in connection with the House of Bethany, where there is a home for girls at Cape Mount. Here she has treated between six thousand and eight thousand sufferers each year, and made in addition uncounted visits far into the country to relieve the sick who could not come to her. These journeys are often of the hardest, through tropic jungles or miles into the interior by canoe. It is encouraging to have her testimony that everywhere she has been treated with greatest courtesy and grateful appreciation of all she does."

Dr. and Mrs. Cammack, missionaries of the American Board, both of them physicians, were recently sent to Western Africa, where they are beginning their work at Chisamba. They had not been there long when Mrs. Cammack wrote of their surroundings to a personal friend. We cannot better describe the work of the medical missionary in Africa than by quoting from this letter:

The medical work here is enough to keep our hands full now, and is growing all the time. If it continues to grow after this fashion you will have to send us out more doctors before long. We have from forty to sixty patients each day, and all sorts of cases, some of them very interesting and others serious and sometimes incurable, though some things which are considered almost incurable at home seem to respond better to treatment here. We have done as few major operations as possible, because of lack of equipment, etc., though we hope to get things in better shape for such work when our last order of medical and hospital supplies arrives.

Our work is more than paying expenses already. We took in more than enough the first month to pay the initial cost of our six months' supplies of drugs. Of course, every month may not average as well; it could hardly be expected to do so, but I have been surprised at the amount that has come in. It is this work that has taken Mr. Cammack away from home so much, and it cannot be helped when doctors are so far apart. It takes so long to get to and from cases. It will be a long time yet before the railroad gets up even this far, and then it will be available for travel in only two directions. Well, we'll just have to pray a little harder for the Lord to open somebody's pocket-book at home and send us out some more workers. I hate to ask for more here, when I know there are so many other countries needing them so badly, too; but the destitution and the ignorance and superstition and terrible native practices upon those who are sick are appalling sometimes.

One who makes glad. Dr. Stauffacher's hospital at Gikuki, Portuguese East Africa, is one of the most remarkable missionary institutions in Africa. The hospital staff consists of one foreign physician, one foreign nurse, and two native medical assistants. During the year there were:

In-patients	300
Operations under total anaesthetic	10
Minor operations	286
First Visits	1,800
Return Visits	980
Itinerating treatments	370
Itinerating Visits	445

The hospital has two medical classes with nine men and *twelve women*, the only available assistants being those whom he trains, perforce, himself.

As for his native patients, their opinion is quaintly expressed in the following letter sent by one to the Board of Foreign Missions of the Methodist Episcopal Church:

"This doctor,—we call him in our native converse, 'Nenguelisam,' that means interpret, 'Maker of people to be glad,' " so runs the letter. "Oh, this marvelously doctor! Why? Look at the people; these did have great sick which we could not hope that these people will be healed. But now are getting well. Is he not marvelously doctor? He is doctor of hearts, too. He makes happy the unjoy hearts and makes more tenderness the durable hearts. He is a friend of babies, children, men, women, white people, and he is friend of all people of black. If he finds us at food he take the spoon and eat with us the food of our black people. Therefore, I make you know that you not fatigue to help this make-glad Doctor Stauffacher."

A wedding journey. It was a remarkable wedding journey for the young missionaries, Dr. and Mrs. Arthur L. Piper, from New York to Kapanga in 1914; the last stage of it was trekked over the caravan trail through the forest for eight weeks with the little band of carrier boys, laden with the equipment and medical supplies. It brought these brave pioneers to their new home, three hundred miles from any other Protestant missionary in any direction, and here they alone ministered in body, mind, and soul to the pitifully needy community for three years, until Miss Marie Jensen, a nurse, and Mr. and Mrs. Thomas B. Brinton joined them. A very unusual reenforcement to this mission station has come from time to time from the freed slaves, who have returned to this, their original home, after years of bondage and many of whom have become Christian through the influence of missionaries in the coast towns, to which they were carried in slavery. With their aid a church, a school, and now a hospital, given in memory of Mrs. Piper's mother, have been built and the good tidings are being borne to "the regions beyond."

Dr. Mabie: an appreciation. "For a year she has moved among us, a beloved presence, a face instinct with sincerity, sympathy, kindliness, and character, a way with her peculiar to those who have hearts at leisure from themselves.

"She belonged to us, and yet we knew that she belonged in a still deeper sense to Africa and that she longed to be about her Father's business. Most of us would prefer Boston to the Belgian Congo, but Catherine Mabie's heart was true to "the Lord's black sheep" deep in the African jungle. But how can the doctor cross all the seas between, we asked ourselves, with the assassins of the deep ever lurking to accomplish their errands of destruction? It is no time for a woman to start on a three-months-long journey; let her wait until these troubles are over.

"Such counsels were met with the comment, 'Pray us through!' and steady preparation for departure; the doctor was too wonted to perils on land to be daunted by perils on the sea. And so we waved her goodbye, the intrepid little lady with her firm faith in the unseen, torpedo-proof, and that yearning love for her poor people which many waters cannot quench.

"What did she see before her at her journey's end? In her own words, a maze of ignorance, superstition and fear; a native thought-plane wholly different from her own; an unwritten language; black-skinned women, not secluded, not even protected by a single garment; a long season of fierce tropical heat with torrential rains to fill the air with steam; a small dispensary; about its door,—ever waiting,—a crowd of half-naked, dirty, heathen mothers with their sick babies; children loathsome with skin diseases; abscesses needing the knife; childless wives seeking children; sorrowful women whose children all die at birth, a folk sin-sick and sorrow-worn who marvel much to find somewhere on earth the touch of love and healing.

"But this is not all Dr. Mabie sees. She has not lived in Congoland twenty years for nothing. Her woman's wit teaches her to make a home even here. She sees a rolling valley at the foot of beautiful hills, along whose base flows the river; on a green knoll above the valley she sees a cluster of airy bungalows, brick dwellings and grass-thatched sheds; around these are well-kept lawns, broad paths bordered with citronella, cocoanut palms and roses. It is an ordered settlement where whole families are taught wholesome human conditions of life. In one bungalow is a fair chamber she can call her own, a retreat for the hours when the multitude scatter to their homes, or the long medical itinerary through the jungle has come to an end. Life here for her is far from impossible; the lives of others are precious, and the doctor sees already in her mind's eye what is soon to be hers at Kimpese,—the small maternity and children's hospital, which the people at home have promised her as the crown of her first twenty years of service in Congoland. This is what lies at the end of the long journey, this, and the communion of the white saints and the adoring love of the black would-be saints of Kimpese whom she is seeking to bring to His feet. Who does not wish Catherine Mabie twenty years more of blessed service in the Name of the Great Physician?"

A Congo General Conference. The Seventh Annual Conference of Congo Protestant Missionaries was held at Luebo, a station of the American Presbyterian Church, South, where seventy-three missionaries made up the largest Congo General Conference ever held. They said, "We recognized as never before the power stored up in this combination and union of Protestant Societies." The medical session was of great helpfulness, and Dr. F. P. Lynch of the American Baptist Mission, in his plea for better equipment, said:

"The first substantial hospital for the Congolese was located at Mukimvika on simple yet ample lines of construction, with a large central room, well-lighted and airy, for general use as a dispensary and for operations and surgical dressings. Two wards are in direct connection, each one having the normal capacity of twenty beds, which are made of pitch pine, six feet by three, provided with a native mat and blankets. San Salvador followed with larger equipment, more buildings, and the important addition of a trained nurse to the staff. Bolobo has expanded on still larger lines of equipment and efficiency. The American Baptist Mission has suddenly made a signal advance in providing ample funds for four new hospitals. With the completion of the hospitals, the appropriation for the service at each hospital will advance from $200 a year to $1,200, a change which seems magical and inspiring to medical missionaries. A trained nurse with a corps of native assistants will be provided for each hospital. In the far, fair lands of Christian development, the hospital has become as much a mark of progressive Christianity as college or cathedral, and here in Congo it should be maintained in representative standing for the honor of His Service in the Wilderness."

The appeal of Africa.   In November, 1917, a conference on the Christian Occupation of Africa was held in New York City. From an address on that occasion by Bishop Lambuth, Methodist Episcopal, South, we give a few sentences summing up the appeal of Africa.

"To make Christ known to the unreached millions in remote sections the way must be pioneered for the Gospel, superstition dispelled and the bondage to fear broken. Christianity, presented in the concrete by the medical missionary, wins where nothing else will. The medical missionary in Africa is held in high regard by the native. . . . The supply of doctors in East, West, and Central Africa is utterly inadequate; there are too few women practitioners and the number of nurses is entirely too small. . . . With the exception of four medical missionaries for the Sudan, two for the Belgian Congo, and four nurses, they are all at work around the rim of the continent."

Bishop Lambuth makes, among others, the following recommendations:

1. A survey of the field, especially the tropical zone, with reference to the location of hospitals in connection with mission stations.

2. A call for a larger number of medical missionaries, men and women, and of trained nurses, the latter to be women of more than average experience.

3. Co-ordination of plans and co-operation of effort upon the part of Boards and Societies.

4. A systematic fight against poisonous insects.

5. The establishment of small but well-equipped hospitals and dispensaries, at every central station, two doctors and one nurse forming the staff.

6. The throwing of a line of stations buttressed with hospitals and dispensaries, right across the continent, through French Equatorial Africa, two hundred and fifty miles apart, to check the Mohammedan advance.

Theodore Roosevelt has declared that "the good done by missionary effort in Africa has been incalculable." But the future must see works like these and yet greater works if Africa is to be redeemed.

2. THE PROMISE OF THE FUTURE

"Go, Let go, Help go."

Isabella Bird Bishop.

It remains for us to take a final glance over the lands in which we have seen the Battalion of Life at work.

India has in round numbers a population of three hundred and fifteen millions. Here we find under missionary* control one hundred and eighty-three hospitals, three hundred and seventy-six dispensaries, one hundred and twenty-two men and one hundred and fifty-nine women physicians.

China, with a population of more than four hundred millions, has three hundred and seventy-two mission hospitals, three hundred and twenty-eight

* All statistics relate to missionary, not general, equipment.

dispensaries, two hundred and sixty-seven men and ninety-three women medical missionaries.

For Korea's sixteen millions we have twenty-nine hospitals, thirty-one dispensaries, thirty-one men and five women medical missionaries.

The Philippine Islands, with a population of nine millions, have ten hospitals, and eighteen dispensaries under missionary conduct, with fourteen men and two women physicians.

Siam, with about the same population as the Philippines, has ten hospitals, twenty dispensaries, thirteen medical missionaries; all men, no women.

Persia's population is nine millions, five hundred thousand. For this number of people she has ten hospitals, seventeen dispensaries, thirteen men and six women medical missionaries.

Arabia has a population of one million, five hundred and ninety-six thousand, one hundred and sixty-five. Here are five hospitals, eight dispensaries, four men and four women medical missionaries.

Turkey and Syria show about twenty millions population. Here are thirty-five hospitals, fifty dispensaries, forty-eight men and ten women physicians.

For Egypt's twelve and one-half millions we have ten hospitals, sixteen dispensaries, twelve men and two women physicians.

Africa—a continent, not a country,—confronts us with its one hundred and thirty-six millions. For these the hospitals number eighty-five, the dispensaries two hundred and twenty-eight, the men physicians one hundred and six, the women physicians fifteen, of whom but five are American.

Native physicians demanded.   Africa, Siam, and Arabia have no native physicians. The other countries under survey show a small number (male and female taken together) varying from one hundred and seventy-two in China to four in Egypt and one in Persia. Small, indeed, is this accession to the Battalion of Life, but in this body of new recruits dwells the promise of the future. For the figures which we have presented, giving the results of a century of medical missions, tell nothing more loudly than that the people of these lands can never be effectually served in their dire need by foreign physicians. *They must come to their own aid.* The women of India, China, and of the Moslem world, must themselves become medical missionaries to their own sisters. Dr. Moorshead truly says, "The little band of women doctors sent out to such lands as India and China, including those laboring in a non-mission capacity, can never by themselves alone touch more than a fringe of the suffering womanhood of these great fields." The emphasis must be laid upon the native medical woman.

New recruits called for.   This means not a slackening of the stream of missionary endeavor, but an imperative demand for its increase. How can these native girls practice the art of healing unless they themselves first be taught? And how shall they be taught without a teacher?

In all our upper grade mission schools for girls in heathen countries there are pupils who show character and capacity for the study and practice of medicine. Certain of these, but few indeed, have traveled far from home and in Europe or the United States

have prepared themselves to serve their own people.
This is good and very good, but it is not good enough.
The way is very long; the process costly and difficult,
the separation from the native land for a term of
years fraught with divisive and unfavorable possibilities. What then?

India shows the way. In the crucible of high missionary
consultation there has been produced,
as the final residuum, after all other plans and
purposes have been evaporated, the necessity of
native schools on native ground for the training of
native women in medicine in all lands open to foreign
missions. This solution of a serious problem remains
outstanding, in great degree unattained, but not
unattainable. The beginning has been made. We
look naturally to India, eldest of our fields of labor.
Yes, India can show the way. There are now in
working order two schools of medicine for women,
conducted under missionary control,—one in the
north, at Ludhiana, one in the south at Vellore.

Ludhiana. Mention has been made in a preceding chapter of Miss Hewlett, the
English missionary who began her pioneer work for
women at Amritsar in the Punjab in 1880. Her place
in medical work for the women of Northern India
is assured, and the North India School at Ludhiana
is in a sense her monument. In 1894, Miss Hewlett
threw her experience into the organizing of this
school, and clinical opportunities for its first students
were drawn from her own extensive medical practice. Later the Government extended partial support
to the undertaking, but it remains definitely Christian and definitely union in its management and

control, and is sustained in large part by a union of the various missionary agencies at work in the peninsula.

From the circular letter of 1917-18 issued by the London Auxiliary Committee we give the following passages:

The Ludhiana College gives to the Missionary Societies an opportunity such as may never occur again of associating themselves with a great renaissance. The proportion of young women qualified by education to take up medical study is far greater among the Christians than in other sections of the population. In addition to these, the College admits, by arrangement with Government, a certain number of non-Christians, who pass their student life under Christian influence of the most inspiring kind, although none are compelled to attend Christian services. Thus, if it were enabled to work up to its full strength, *such a supply of good women would be ensured as would leaven this new branch of the medical profession throughout. This would mean a silent impact of the Christian faith on the domestic life of the country such as has never been attained hitherto*. The last generation of missionaries, with true insight, threw themselves into the front of the rising desire for education, with the result that Bible truth has permeated the educated classes to a degree that is very far from being indicated by the number of avowed converts. *Will their successors of today let slip a still greater opportunity—greater for this reason, that it is even more important to influence the wives and mothers than the men?*

For more than twenty years Dr. Edith Brown has

been patiently working, with a self-sacrifice to which human praise seems inappropriate. She is assisted by a staff of able women who are content to live on a subsistence allowance, all fees from private patients being paid to the funds of the College. The fees received by Dr. Edith Brown for her professional services outside the College in 1915-16 amounted to £1,100, all of which was given to the College.

The students find not only a thoroughly efficient school, but also a Christian home, where they pass several impressionable years under the daily personal influence of accomplished and devout Englishwomen. All visitors, both official and private, are deeply impressed with "the atmosphere of studiousness, enthusiasm, purposeful energy, and cheerfulness which pervades the place," to quote the words of the Committee appointed by Government to inspect the College.

A highly competent and impartial observer, Miss MacDougall, now Principal of the Women's Christian College, Madras, wrote: "The excellence of the staff, the efficiency of the hospital and dispensary, the beautiful life open to every student, the high ideal of work and mutual service, seemed hardly open to improvement."

Training is given the students in nursing, compounding, midwifery, and medicine, and they are supplying the need for trained workers in other hospitals and schools. There is great need for more buildings to accommodate students and staff, as well as wards for patients, general and private.

The far-reaching influence of the college will be realized by looking at the map. Students come from

South Madras, Bombay, and Baluchistan; in the West from central India and the United Provinces; the total number under training is one hundred and thirty-five. Most encouraging testimony has been received about the work of various graduates. One doctor who recently visited the college wrote, "Ludhiana Medical College is the hope of India. The graduate we have as our assistant certainly speaks highly for the transformation made there in the lives of Indian girls."

The representatives of the various Mission Boards in South India, in a different climate, in a different language area, and with the same urgent need, have long been planning and praying for a similar institution in the South. Government has looked favorably upon the plan, has granted land and promises annual. aid.

Vellore.   As the English name, Hewlett, of the Amritsar Mission is enshrined in the Medical School at Ludhiana in the North, the American name, Scudder, of the Arcot Mission, is closely associated with that at Vellore in the South.

In 1895, Dr. Louisa H. Hart, then in charge of the medical work for women in the famous Arcot Mission (Reformed Church), perceived that the strategic point for a hospital for women and children was Vellore. Ida Scudder, granddaughter of Dr. John Scudder, first medical missionary to the Orient, was at that time in the United States, having just completed her course in medicine. Upon her was laid the urgent request to the home churches for the means to establish such a hospital. "Doctor Ida" as she is affectionately termed, was successful in this undertaking, the result being the admirable Mary Taber Schell Hospital at Vellore. This was opened in 1903 under the care of Doctors Scudder and Hart and is in all respects signally successful. Ten years later the crying need for a medical school for the native women of the South could no longer be denied, and steps were taken toward its consummation. A Board of Governors (interdenominational) was appointed in America and Great Britain to co-operate with a General Council in India for the establishment of the first Women's Medical College of South India.

It is with deep emotion that we in this far country read in the columns of *The Madras Mail* for "Tuesday evening, August 13, 1918," the account of the formal opening by H. E. Lord Pentland, Governor of Madras. The Governor was welcomed by Dr. Anna S. Kugler, the distinguished head of the Guntur Medical Mission of the American Evangelical Lutheran Church. Dr. Kugler alluded to the fact that the first Principal of the new Medical School (Dr. Ida Scudder) is granddaughter of the first medical missionary to India and a member of a family that has given "eighty-four of its members to labor for the uplift, in body and soul, of the people of India." Space cannot be given here for extracts from the speeches of the Governor and other distinguished guests, all strongly emphasizing the demand for the new institution, nor for the memorial addressed on that occasion to the Governor by Dr. Ida Scudder, a historic document of the first order in interest and importance in the development of medical work in India by women for women.

China not left
behind.

China, where co-education is thus far impracticable, has three schools of medicine for women; that established by the Presbyterian Board, North, in Canton under Dr. Mary Fulton, the Union Medical College at Peking, and the School at Soochow under the Southern Methodist Episcopal Board, with which Dr. Love and Dr. Polk are connected. The last-named institution will doubtless be merged ere long in the proposed Union Medical School of Shanghai. There will then remain three firmly established schools for Chinese women medical students, planted at three strategic points, and of these two will be Union, one only representing a single denomination. This illustrates the strong movement towards missionary consolidation. Here China is leading the way and furnishing a striking example.

Last April there met in Nanking a "Federal Council" composed of delegates from five synods and twenty-two presbyteries and representatives of the London Missionary Society and of the American Board. They formed a federation and took the name "The Allied Church of Jesus Christ in China." Medical schools, theological schools, universities for men and colleges for women are to be under this federated body, instead of under separate denominations, as heretofore, and all Christian churches at work in China are invited to join.

From a vivid description of Peking Union Medical College by Mrs. F. H. Sheets we give interesting information.

For years a medical college for women has been

a dream of Dr. Anna D. Gloss and the pioneer doctors of other missions. A few years ago the denominations working here in Peking formed a plan for union higher educational work for women. A union college of liberal arts was founded and housed upon the Congregational compound; a union medical college was assigned to the Methodist compound; and a union Bible training school of very high grade was designed for the Presbyterian compound. In each case the missionary society upon whose compound the college was located was to be responsible for the building and equipment, and all denominations were to share in making up the faculty and in the running of the school.

It seemed wise to use the old hospital for the medical school, remodeling and adapting it to that purpose, and to put up a new and larger building for the Elizabeth Sleeper Davis Memorial Hospital. Therefore, the women asked for forty thousand dollars from the women at home, with which to buy land and to erect the new building and remodel the old one. They secured a fine piece of land across from the former hospital gate, and there they now have a splendid hospital with accommodations for nurses. The old hospital building, which, by the way, is really not an old building at all—only about ten years—but was called that to distinguish it from the new building, was remodeled and converted into the Union Medical College for Women.

The college offers a five-year course to middle school graduates, but it hopes soon to raise the entrance requirements to include two years in college.

Two classes have already been graduated. The three graduates of last June are in mission hospitals in Shantung and Fukien Provinces.

The American members of the family form an interesting group. One always mentions first Dr. Gloss, whose very heart is built into this institution. Dr. Gloss has been a medical missionary in Peking for more than twenty-five years, and went through the siege of Peking.

Dr. Leonard of the Presbyterian Church is dean of the college, and Dr. Bash, from the same mission, is another member of the faculty.

Dr. Stryker was a Methodist missionary in Foochow, but is now a valuable member of this faculty.

Dr. Manderson, a Methodist Episcopal missionary, has just returned from furlough, during which she took advanced work in the colleges at home, and comes back with splendid preparation and a good knowledge of the language.

And Dr. Heath, who had a most enviable record in college at home, is a Baptist, is supported by an Episcopalian lady, and is working under the Methodist Episcopal Board, having taken work in the college that was begun by a Presbyterian woman.

These doctors are exceptional women and form the nucleus of a proposed faculty of which any institution might be proud. To this faculty are added some of the men physicians from the Union Medical College for Men.

The proposed Union Medical College at Shanghai will have a unique work in China, that of teaching medicine in English to Chinese women. It will not lack for highly qualified pupils from the best homes of China, some of them graduates of the native Union Colleges at Peking and Nanking, and they are eagerly appropriating it and reaching out for more.

The Church now has the opportunity and the privilege through this college to mould the lives of the higher class young women and through them to mould the lives of all the Central China women. If not grasped now, we venture to say that within ten years this opportunity will have passed forever from the hands of the Church. The possibility of the medical profession in China consisting wholly of non-Christian men and women is one to be regarded with grave anxiety.

China's suffering women, the overworked doctors, the closed hospitals are begging for women doctors. The number of women physician missionaries from America seems to be decreasing each year. The Mission Boards appeal in vain for them. Why not train the Chinese women to be physicians? What stands in the way? Not the customs of the country, nor the lack of desire to study medicine, nor the lack of preparation on the part of Chinese women, but the dearth of teaching and equipment.

The prospects of the new Union College at Shanghai are bright indeed. The Woman's Union Missionary Society has most generously offered as foundation for its work the famous Margaret Williamson Hospital (see Chapter III), wonderfully located and equipped. The school will provide training for the present for all Eastern and Central China. With the preparation afforded in science at Ginling College, Nanking, there is every hope that this institution will reach full college grade within a short time.

We pause and look around us and far afield, but the story is told. In all Asia and Africa (save for a small and tentative beginning in Korea), this is the sum of qualified training for native women physicians on native ground under missionary auspices.

But the beginning is made and the prime factor here is not quantity, but quality. In our first chapter we established the point that women have made good as medical missionaries. It is not more difficult to prove that Asiatic women have made good as Christian physicians. In India we point to Dr. Karmarkar and Dr. Joshi and Dr. Ma Sau Sa, referring the reader for a more extended list to the fourth chapter of *Women Workers of the Orient*, by Margaret E. Burton, our last year's study book. It would be a welcome task to sound the praises of these eminent and distinguished medical "trailmakers" for their Hindu sisters, but their story is too well-known to call for repetition here. It is well to convince ourselves that the torch which they have borne is to be handed on to others inspired by like high motives, for others are pressing forward.

The name of Dr. Anna S. Kugler,* for thirty years head of the Lutheran Hospital at Guntur, South India, has long been one to conjure by. We can rely upon Dr. Kugler not to overstate as she introduces to us her assistant in hospital work, Miss P. Paru Ammal, a graduate of Madras Government Medical College.

---

* See *The King's Highway*, H. B. Montgomery, pp. 79 and 80 and *World Missions and Worlds Peace*, C. A. Mason, pp. 206, 207, United Study Series.

She came to us, says Dr. Kugler, in January, 1911, and I hope she will be able to remain with us for some years. She comes from the Malabar Coast, and is eldest daughter of a prominent, high caste Hindu lawyer. That he is singularly liberal is shown by the liberal education which he has given his daughters and by the fact that he has written several books against idolatry and in defence of Christianity. That Miss Paru is herself a Christian she attributes in large measure to her father's teaching of the New Testament.

Coming among us a stranger, she has made for herself a place that any young Indian woman might be glad to have. Just out of college, with no experience, she has gone on from day to day gradually acquiring an experience, so that for months she has done almost all the dispensary work; and so much is she liked by the people that our dispensary attendances have greatly increased, and our average daily attendance has gone from eighty to more than one hundred. Quiet, ladylike, dignified, gentle, and withal intelligent and trained, she can see one hundred and fifty patients of a morning, and then be ready to help in the wards in the afternoon. She is of increasing help in the surgical and maternity work, and it is a great help to have her do the laboratory work. She has also a real missionary spirit, so that she is only too glad to teach a class in the Sunday School, to take a midweek Bible class and to superintend the Bible work at the dispensary.

It is a great pleasure to me to testify to the high opinion I have of her professionally, and to the affection that I have for her as a friend. No one could have been more fortunate in the experiment with a medical assistant, and I hope that when the women of the Church remember us in prayer they will remember, too, our much-loved Miss Paru, who is having such an influence for good among her Indian sisters. It is a new sight in this part of India to see an Indian lady doctor. Already one of the little daughters of the rajah of Ellore has announced that she intends to study medicine and be like Miss Paru.

And now we have a native Telugu girl who has qualified to practice medicine. We hail her as the first of her race to attain this honor; we welcome her to the Battalion of Life. May many follow in her train! Her name is Y. Nandama; her grand-parents were baptized by Dr. Clough on that memorable day when two thousand, two hundred and twenty-two received baptism; her parents are teachers in the Girls' School at Kanagari. When Nandama had graduated from the Girls' High School at Nellore, she entered upon a four years' course in medicine at Ludhiana Medical College, a week's journey from her home, where she was graduated, April, 1918, with the degree of M.P.L. which signifies Medical Practitioner License, the degree of M.D. (to which she would be entitled in our country) not being granted to women in India. Girls of South India henceforth, seeking to follow in Nandama's steps, will not be forced to travel to Ludhiana to obtain their training; Vellore Medical School is now open to them! Nandama is now at work in Nellore in the Baptist Woman's Hospital, and has proved herself steadfast and indispensable under difficult conditions.

Turning now to China, we greet again her two conspicuous pioneers, Mary Stone and Ida Kahn, of whose career we learned somewhat in Chapter III. These two leading spirits in their steadfast devotion to the service of healing among their sisters in China have established beyond question the capacity of the Chinese to serve in the Battalion of Life. Contemporary with these two, and belonging essentially in their group, is Dr. Hü King Eng, head surgeon of the Woolston Memorial Hospital at Foochow. She, like Dr. Stone and Dr. Kahn, came to this country to seek a medical education;

this she secured in the Woman's Medical College of Philadelphia. In 1895, she returned to her native city under appointment as a regular medical missionary of the Woman's Foreign Missionary Society of the Methodist Episcopal Church. As the first Chinese woman to receive the degree of Doctor of Medicine in a foreign land, Dr. Hü King Eng is "an honor to her race and a joy to the Society under whose auspices she works."

Following in her steps we see Li Bi Cu, daughter of Christian Chinese parents, who was brought to America for education in girlhood and graduated with honor from the Woman's Medical College of Philadelphia. On her return to China, in 1905, Dr. Li was appointed head of the Methodist Episcopal Mission Hospital about to be built at Ngucheng, Fukien Province. In addition to the care of her patients this young physician was called upon to oversee the building and furnishing of the new hospital dedicated, in 1907, to the healing of women and children in the name of the Great Physician. Here at her post, through dark days and bright, with no competent assistants, Dr. Li stands, a good soldier of Christ Jesus, keeping forever burning the light in a dark place. In 1911, the report of her hospital showed three hundred and sixty-five in-patients, five thousand, nine hundred and eighty-five visits to the dispensary, five hundred and fifty-seven patients seen in their homes and the total number of patients treated six thousand, eight hundred and ninety-eight. Surely, a brave record!

Time fails us to tell of others, no less worthy, who are laboring heart and soul to save the women and children of their native China from preventable suffering and death. There is Dr. Loh, head physician now in the David Gregg Hospital at Canton, Dr. Tsao in charge of the Friends' Hospital in Nanking, and others who are entering into the labors of these. Dr. Tsao has rendered distinguished service as a lecturer on scientific subjects on the faculty of Ginling College. Margaret E. Burton gives account of an additional number of young Chinese medical women in her interesting book, *The Education of Women in China.*

A Korean girl physician.   In our fourth chapter mention was made of Esther Kim Pak, pupil and protégée of Dr. R. S. Hall in Korea. The name Esther was given the little Korean girl when she was baptized on profession of Christian faith, when about fifteen years of age. At sixteen, she was married to Mr. Pak and her life of active usefulness began. Studying constantly under Dr. Hall in the hospital at Seoul she became familiar with the symptoms and treatment of disease; the purpose of studying medicine was aroused. When Dr. Hall decided to return for a time to America after the death of her husband, Esther begged to go with her that she might pursue her cherished desire of studying medicine. Both husband and wife, accordingly, accompanied Mrs. Hall and Esther set herself steadily to gain the training she so coveted. Her persistence was fairly heroic. Mrs. Hall went back to Korea; Mr. Pak died of tuberculosis, but still she stood fast by her purpose.

In 1896, Esther entered the Woman's Medical College of Baltimore, the first Korean woman to take up the study of medicine. Here she obtained her degree in the year 1900, and then, bereft of her young husband, she hastened back alone to Korea, three years after Mrs. Hall had returned thither.

For ten years Dr. Esther Pak labored with whole-souled devotion for her own people. "She was always ready with trained skill and loving sympathy to help them in the dispensary clinic, the hospital ward, or in their humble homes. She was also of great assistance in the Bible Institutes for women, teaching most enthusiastically any subject required from hygiene to church history.

"May 28, 1909, was a crowning day for her and for those who had tried to awaken a deep interest in the education of Korea's daughters as well as sons. That day the Woman's Educational and the Woman's Enterprise Societies combined in showing honors to Korea's first women college graduates, Mrs. Esther Kim Pak, M.D., and Mrs. N. K. Ha, M.A. They were invited to the capital, and were conveyed by carriages in grand style to the old Mulberry Palace grounds, where addresses were delivered, appropriate gold medals awarded to each, followed by a collation. The picture of Dr. Pak, in her college cap and gown, was taken at this time; it shows the gold medal with which she was decorated, and of which she was justly proud. But already disease had laid its hand upon the young doctor. After several years of a brave, but losing battle with tuberculosis, she laid down her work here, April 13, 1910, to receive her coronation on high. Who will take up her work?—a work now so overwhelming that it cannot possibly be met with a few foreign doctors."

Dr. Baldomera Esteban, a native Filipina, a graduate of the Medical Department of Philippine University, is the first interne to serve the Mary J. Johnston Hospital. Tributes to her devotion, skill, and purpose are emphatic. We hail in her the pioneer of her people. We are now only in the earliest stage of Christian medical missions in these Islands which are under our own American Government; great is the promise if the Churches of America awake to their responsibility.

Women Physicians for Siam. Three members of the teaching force of the Harriet M. House School for Girls at Bangkok, Siam, have gone this last year to Manila, Philippine Islands, to take up the study of medicine and nursing, two of them to fit themselves to become the first women physicians in Siam, and the third to become a trained nurse. One of the young women medical students is the sister of a graduate of Harvard University who is soon to return to Siam as a civil engineer. The other is the daughter of the Attorney-General of Siam.

As we reflect upon these native women physicians whose names have now rapidly passed in review, with those others which might be added, the conclusion is—*fit, but few*. Among the suffering and neglected millions of their sisters the number is indeed piteously inadequate, and inadequate it must remain unless reinforcements are sent and sent without delay to the Battalion of Life. The medical woman who goes to heathen peoples goes not merely to minister to the sick and suffering, not chiefly to break down, by the power of her presence, the walls which shut in the Oriental woman or hold as a beast of burden the African woman; she goes to act as herald, exemplar, teacher and guide for the awakening womanhood of the nations "afar off."

For the women of heathendom there must be for generations to come, in time of sickness, utter neglect or the service of their own sex. *"By women doctors alone,"* says Dr. Moorshead (the italics are his) *"can the very great amount of pitiful suffering prevailing amongst immense multitudes of heathen and Moslem women be effectually alleviated or cured."** This point needs no further emphasis; it has the emphasis of every chapter of our book. From the heathen point of view woman's function is to serve and to suffer; let her serve, let her suffer, her death is no great matter.

At the call of need overseas in these last four years all over our country girls and women have sprung to their feet, ready to go, ready to do to the limit of their strength, to dare and to die in ministration to the wounded soldiers of a score of nations. And now the call to go still comes, not less loud, more piercing yet in its insistence; your sisters in Asia and Africa agonize and suffer needless death from cruel neglect and worse every hour of every day. You can help, you can heal, you can save. Hasten to their relief.

Human experience has produced no challenge more poignant, no service more gloriously rewarded, than that of medical missions. The discipline of sacrifice,

---

* *The Appeal of Medical Missions.*   R. S. Moorshead, Fleming H. Revell Company, 1913.

the blessedness of casting off the bonds of ease for heroic ends which our young American women have of late been set to learn, must not be a passing thing; it must not fail of its deeper working. The ministry of healing for the women of Asia and Africa today sounds a summons which the women of America must meet—will meet—no less nobly than they have met the call to the war zone of Europe.

———————

Surely the future looks black enough, yet it holds a hope, a single hope. One, and one power only, can arrest the descent and save us. That is the Christian religion. Democracy is but a side issue. The paramount issue underlying the issue of Democracy is the religion of Christ and Him crucified; the bedrock of civilization; the source and resource of all that is worth having in the world that is, that gives promise in the world to come; not as an abstraction; not as a huddle of sects and factions; but as a mighty force and principle of being. . . . If the world is to be saved from destruction—it will be saved alone by the Christian religion.

Henry Watterson.

The missionary enterprise is the one indisputably Christian flag flying at present; it is the only answer that the Church can make to a world at war. Here is our substitute for the way of war actually at work; here is the other way which we are being challenged to show. To go forth to uncivilized or hostile peoples with no force behind one but the love of God and no wages asked but to share the suffering of Christ is the real redemptive enterprise.

W. E. Orchard.

INDEX